The Spirit of
Christmas

G.K. CHESTERTON
The Spirit of Christmas

STORIES ❦ POEMS ❦ ESSAYS

SELECTED AND ARRANGED BY

Marie Smith

Xanadu

British Library Cataloguing in Publication Data

Chesterton, G.K.
  The spirit of Christmas
  I. Title   II. Smith, Marie
  828'.91209   PR4453.C4

  ISBN 0–947761–07–1
  ISBN 0–947761–08–X Pbk

First published 1984 by Xanadu Publications Limited
5 Uplands Road, London N8 9NN

Distributed by WHS Distributors, Leicester

Set by Wyvern Typesetting Limited, Bristol

Printed and bound in Great Britain by
Richard Clay (The Chaucer Press), Bungay, Suffolk

CONTENTS

INTRODUCTION

'I should like,' wrote Maisie Ward in her biography of G. K. Chesterton, 'to collect all the essays and poems on Christmas; he wrote several every year, yet each is different, each goes to the heart of his thought ... Some men, it may be, are best moved to reform by hate, but Chesterton was best moved by love and nowhere does that love shine more clearly than in all he wrote about Christmas. It will be for this philosophy, this charity, this poetry that men will turn over the pages of *G.K.'s Weekly* a century hence if the world still lasts.' Re-reading Chesterton's Christmas poems after a gap of far too many years the same thought occurred to me, and when I discovered that not only the poems, but the Christmas essays and stories too, were out of print and unavailable, the passing thought became a solid project. Much later, it became the solid object that you are holding.

The collection spans the whole of Chesterton's writing career, and I have arranged it in a broadly chronological sequence. The first piece in the book—the short poem under the heading 'Xmas Day'—is from Chesterton's notebook, begun in 1894 when he was emerging from a long period of doubt and self-torment into a mood of Whitman-influenced optimism that was to be the foundation-stone of his developing philosophy. Some of the poems later published in *The Wild Knight* and *Poems* exist in various drafts composed about this time, and it is perhaps worth making the point that the young man who wrote them was most emphatically not the huge, caped figure of the caricatures; when we think of Chesterton we automatically see him as he was at the height of his fame—the image is irresistible—but that came much later. In the 1890s he was tall and slim, with an unruly mane of chestnut hair, working as a publisher's assistant and by no means committed to Christianity, let alone to Catholicism: that too came much later. The poems that I have grouped together in the first section of the book ('A Child is Born') belong to this transitional stage in Chesterton's life, although it is difficult to date them precisely. 'The Wise Men', for instance, was first collected in the *Poems* of 1915, but a shorter version was used in a Christmas card sent by the Chestertons to their friends in 1913, and further delving reveals that it appeared in *The Daily News* as early as 1905. It may well have been written earlier still; at any rate, it seems to belong stylistically with the earliest poems and, rightly or wrongly, that is where I have put it.

The next three sections cover the great days of Chesterton's career, when he was pouring out books of essays, verse, artistic and literary criticism, short stories and novels, appearing on debating platforms all over the place with Wells, Shaw and the other great figures of the age, and writing regular and avidly-read columns in a number of newspapers and magazines, only a small proportion of which have been collected in book form. At Christmas, every editor seemed to want a contribution from GKC—and many of them got one. Choosing from this vast output has not been an easy task, and I have tried in the space available to include as wide a variety of subjects as possible. Chesterton is always interesting, but he had his own pet themes—Dickens was one, Christmas as a pagan festival another—and to avoid repetition I have, perhaps rather ruthlessly, extracted what I think is best from some of the longer pieces. I cannot imagine that any editor feels very comfortable about doing this, although in Chesterton's case there are plenty of precedents: *A Chesterton Calendar* was compiled by his wife, and other anthologies made in his lifetime followed the same pattern. I have sometimes been able to use extracts taken from these earlier collections, but elsewhere I have had to make my own. For this cavalier treatment I offer my apologies, but so much of Chesterton's work is out of print that, given the opportunity to put together a new collection, the temptation to include as much of it as possible was unavoidable. What is quite certain is that Chesterton himself, horribly careless of his own work once it was finished, would not have minded in the least.

On the positive side, it has enabled me to include quite a lot of hitherto uncollected material from the pages of *The Daily News*, *The Illustrated London News* and a number of other publications. Perhaps the rarest of all Chesterton's books—only a handful of bound copies are known to exist—is *The Turkey and the Turk*. This belongs to the period after the Great War and after Chesterton's near-fatal illness, when he was committed to editing and publishing his late brother's paper, which eventually turned into *G.K.'s Weekly*, in whose pages *The Turkey and the Turk* first appeared. It is scarcely a major work, yet read in the right spirit it is a delightful thing, and I am glad to be able to include it here in its entirety, for it will be new to all but the most avid collectors.

The later essays belong to the period of Chesterton's conversion to the Catholic Church, which eventually came in 1922. If there is a change in tone—less of sheer high spirits, a greater anger with the worldly world and, later, a feeling of spiritual serenity at last —there is no dramatic change of attitude. Those early poems and these essays seem to be, in the end, all of a piece; it is, perhaps the consistency not of a man standing still but of a man travelling steadily in a straight line. If the early conflicts produced the finest imaginative and poetic writing, the later work goes deeper. *The Everlasting Man* is generally considered to be Chesterton's best work in this vein, but after much thought I decided not to remove from it the section dealing with the birth of Christ, for it is part of the longer story and that, at least, must be read as a whole. Happily, it is one of the handful of Chesterton's books that is constantly in print—the Father Brown books are the others—and the interested reader should have no difficulty in obtaining a copy.

Even towards the end of his life, Chesterton was capable of surprises. 'The New Christmas', unsigned in the pages of *G.K.'s Weekly* and, I suspect, unread ever since, is a grim little parable of the future—a science-fiction story, in fact, and quite unlike any other tale he wrote. The last poem, 'Gloria in Profundis', has never been included in any edition of the *Collected Poems* and will therefore be new to most readers. As Christopher Hollis remarks, 'He wrote in paradoxes because he thought that the ultimate nature of truth lay in paradoxes, and above all in the supreme Christian paradox by which the Creator of the universe was a little baby, lying in a manger, the child of a human mother.' Or as Chesterton put it, 'Glory to God in the lowest.'

Chesterton died in 1936. During his lifetime he had published more than a hundred books, and posthumous collections added considerably to this total but, as I have said, only a few remain in print, and his critical reputation—whether as poet, novelist, critic or theologian—has for a long time been in eclipse. There are signs that is is changing; W. H. Auden and Kingsley Amis have made excellent selections from his prose, the *Collected Poems* have been reissued in the U.S.A., and the recently-formed Chesterton Society has been doing excellent work in reprinting his writing and providing an outlet for criticism in its journal. Chesterton's books, once plentiful in the second-hand shops, have become virtually unobtainable. I hope that this collection will satisfy to some extent this new appetite for his work, and perhaps win some new admirers for this great, good man. Above all, I hope that it may add something to the enjoyment and understanding of Christmas for all who read it.

My thanks are due to Alison Bailey, indefatigable explorer of the more obscure reaches of the British Library, who collected many of the uncollected pieces herein; to A. P. Watt Ltd, agents for the Chesterton Estate, who have been extremely helpful throughout; and of course to Dorothy Collins, to whom all Chestertonians owe so much.

—Marie Smith

I

A Child is Born

EARLY POEMS, 1894-1900

XMAS DAY ❧

Good news: but if you ask me what it is, I know not;
It is a track of feet in the snow,
It is a lantern showing a path,
It is a door set open.

THE NATIVITY ❧

The thatch on the roof was as golden,
    Though dusty the straw was and old,
The wind had a peal as of trumpets,
    Though blowing and barren and cold,
The mother's hair was a glory
    Though loosened and torn,
For under the eaves in the gloaming
        A child was born.

Have a myriad children been quickened,
    Have a myriad children grown old,
Grown gross and unloved and embittered,
    Grown cunning and savage and cold?
God abides in a terrible patience,
    Unangered, unworn,
And again for the child that was squandered
        A child is born.

What know we of aeons behind us,
    Dim dynasties lost long ago,
Huge empires, like dreams unremembered,
    Huge cities for ages laid low?
This at least—that with blight and with blessing,
    With flower and with thorn,
Love was there, and his cry was among them,
        'A child is born.'

Though the darkness be noisy with systems,
    Dark fancies that fret and disprove,
Still the plumes stir around us, above us
    The wings of the shadow of love:

Oh! princes and priests, have ye seen it
   Grow pale through your scorn;
Huge dawns sleep before us, deep changes,
      A child is born.

And the rafters of toil still are gilded
   With the dawn of the stars of the heart,
And the wise men draw near in the twilight,
   Who are weary of learning and art,
And the face of the tyrant is darkened,
   His spirit is torn,
For a new king is enthroned; yea, the sternest,
      A child is born.

And the mother still joys for the whispered
   First stir of unspeakable things,
Still feels that high moment unfurling
   Red glory of Gabriel's wings.
Still the babe of an hour is a master
   Whom angels adorn,
Emmanuel, prophet, anointed,
      A child is born.

And thou, that art still in thy cradle,
   The sun being crown for thy brow,
Make answer, our flesh, make an answer,
   Say, whence art thou come—who art thou?
Art thou come back on earth for our teaching
   To train or to warn—?
Hush—how may we know?—knowing only
      A child is born.

A CHRISTMAS CAROL 🥀

The Christ-child lay on Mary's lap,
   His hair was like a light.
(O weary, weary were the world,
   But here is all aright.)

The Christ-child lay on Mary's breast,
    His hair was like a star.
(O stern and cunning are the kings,
    But here the true hearts are.)

The Christ-child lay on Mary's heart,
    His hair was like a fire.
(O weary, weary is the world,
    But here the world's desire.)

The Christ-child stood at Mary's knee,
    His hair was like a crown,
And all the flowers looked up at Him,
    And all the stars looked down.

JOSEPH 🦋

If the stars fell; night's nameless dreams
    Of bliss and blasphemy came true,
If skies were green and snow were gold,
    And you loved me as I love you;

O long light hands and curled brown hair,
    And eyes where sits a naked soul;
Dare I even then draw near and burn
    My fingers in the aureole?

Yes, in the one wise foolish hour
    God gives this strange strength to a man.
He can demand, though not deserve,
    Where ask he cannot, seize he can.

But once the blood's wild wedding o'er,
    Were not dread his, half dark desire,
To see the Christ-child in the cot,
    The Virgin Mary by the fire?

THE WISE MEN 🐟

Step softly, under snow or rain,
   To find the place where men can pray;
The way is all so very plain
   That we may lose the way.

Oh, we have learnt to peer and pore
   On tortured puzzles from our youth,
We know all labyrinthine lore,
We are the three wise men of yore,
   And we know all things but the truth.

We have gone round and round the hill
   And lost the wood among the trees,
And learnt long names for every ill,
And served the mad gods, naming still
   The furies the Eumenides.

The gods of violence took the veil
   Of vision and philosophy,
The Serpent that brought all men bale,
He bites his own accursed tail,
   And calls himself Eternity.

Go humbly . . . it has hailed and snowed . . .
   With voices low and lanterns lit;
So very simple is the road,
   That we may stray from it.

The world grows terrible and white,
   And blinding white the breaking day;
We walk bewildered in the light,
For something is too large for sight,
   And something much too plain to say.

The Child that was ere worlds begun
   (. . . We need but walk a little way,
We need but see a latch undone . . .)
The Child that played with moon and sun
   Is playing with a little hay.

The house from which the heavens are fed,
　The old strange house that is our own,
Where tricks of words are never said,
And Mercy is as plain as bread,
　And Honour is as hard as stone.

Go humbly, humble are the skies,
　And low and large and fierce the Star;
So very near the Manger lies
　That we may travel far.

Hark! Laughter like a lion wakes
　To roar to the resounding plain,
And the whole heaven shouts and shakes,
　For God Himself is born again,
And we are little children walking
　Through the snow and rain.

II

Sausages and Stars

ESSAYS, COMMENT AND A STORY

CHRISTMAS THAT IS COMING ❧

There is no more dangerous or disgusting habit than that of celebrating Christmas before it comes, as I am doing in this article. It is the very essence of a festival that it breaks upon one brilliantly and abruptly, that at one moment the great day is not and the next moment the great day is. Up to a certain specific instant you are feeling ordinary and sad; for it is only Wednesday. At the next moment your heart leaps up and your soul and body dance together like lovers; for in one burst and blaze it has become Thursday. I am assuming (of course) that you are a worshipper of Thor, and that you celebrate his day once a week, possibly with human sacrifice. If, on the other hand, you are a modern Christian Englishman, you hail (of course) with the same explosion of gaiety the appearance of the English Sunday. But I say that whatever the day is that is to you festive or symbolic, it is essential that there should be a quite clear black line between it and the time going before. And all the old wholesome customs in connection with Christmas were to the effect that one should not touch or see or know or speak of something before the actual coming of Christmas Day. Thus, for instance, children were never given their presents until the actual coming of the appointed hour. The presents were kept tied up in brown-paper parcels, out of which an arm of a doll or the leg of a donkey sometimes accidentally stuck. I wish this principle were adopted in respect of modern Christmas ceremonies and publications. Especially it ought to be observed in connection with what are called the Christmas numbers of magazines. The editors of the magazines bring out their Christmas numbers so long before the time that the reader is more likely to be still lamenting for the turkey of last year than to have seriously settled down to a solid anticipation of the turkey which is to come. Christmas numbers of magazines ought to be tied up in brown paper and kept for Christmas Day. On consideration, I should favour the editors being tied up in brown paper. Whether the leg or arm of an editor should ever be allowed to protrude I leave to individual choice.

THE CHRISTMAS BALLADS ❧

It is in the old Christmas carols, the carols which date from the Middle Ages, that we find not only what makes Christmas poetic and soothing and stately, but first and foremost what makes Christmas exciting. The exciting quality of Christmas rests on an ancient and admitted paradox. It rests upon the great paradox that the power and centre of the whole universe may be found in some seemingly small matter, that the stars in their courses may move like a moving wheel round the neglected outhouse of an inn. When Walt Whitman said 'There is no object so soft but it makes a hub for the wheeled universe' he expressed unconsciously what is the thrilling element in the story of Bethlehem. And it is extraordinary to notice how completely this feeling of the paradox of the manger was lost by the brilliant and ingenious theologians, and how completely it was kept in the Christmas carols. They, at least, never forgot that the main business of the story they had to tell was that the absolute once ruled the universe from a cattle stall.

It is instructive, for example, to compare the cloudy pomposity of ordinary hymnology with the vigour and precision of the Christian idea in the old carol of 'When Joseph was a-walking'. By means of the plain antithesis of the old ballad, without the use of a single adjective, the fundamental idea of the Christ child is conveyed.

> He neither shall be born,
>   In housen nor in hall,
>   Nor in the place of Paradise,
> But in an ox's stall.
>
> He neither shall be christened
>   In white wine nor in red,
>   But in the fair spring water,
> Where we were christenèd.

Thus across the ages, filled more and more with dogmas and explanations and all the unending madness of the intellect, there comes to us in this nameless and wandering ballad the essential and tremendous claim of Christmas, the paradox on which it was built. Theologians have sought more and more to insist on the separation of Christ from humanity; it was the poetic inspiration of the old ballad-monger that he saw that the thrill of the divinity consisted in the completeness and perfection of the disguise. It is in his work that we realise that Christianity conquered because of the stunning insolence of its paradox, the paradox that a certain

Everlasting Essence when it chose to become a man, chose, with a certain superb irony, to become one of the humblest of men.

There is another fine old carol which I will mention in explaining my meaning. It is the carol in which is told the story of Stephen the Martyr. Careful historians of that period will be interested in learning, for the first time, that,

> Stephen was a steward,
> In King Herodë's hall,

and that he was a personal witness to the appearance of the Star of Bethlehem. King Herod, finding that the condition of a mystic accorded ill with the functions of a steward, summoned him to explain his reasons for wishing to leave the palace.

> Lacketh thee either meat or drink
> In King Herodë's hall?

Stephen answers, with the whole artistic energy of the Christian idea in his words:

> Lacketh me neither meat nor drink
> In King Herodë's hall:
> There is a child in Bethlem born
> Is better than we all.

The utter logical irrelevance and the sublime spiritual relevance of the connection between the first couplet and the last is the summary of all enthusiasm.

There is a small and vulgar fashion of discouraging carols at Christmas. People who chat cheerfully amid all the infernal noises of the underground, people who endure the rattle of a thousand vehicles over a stony road, pretend that they dislike the sound of Christmas carols. To pretend to like a thing may be a sin: to pretend to dislike a thing comes near to the sin against the Holy Ghost. At least it may be hoped that a few at this season may listen to these songs: they are the last echoes of the cry that renewed the world.

Christmas and hygiene are commonly in some antagonism, and I, for one, am heartily on the side of Christmas. Glancing down a newspaper column I see the following alarming sentence: 'The *Lancet* adds a frightful corollary that the only way to eat Christmas pudding with perfect impunity is to eat it alone.' At first the meaning of this sentence deceived me. I thought it meant that the eater of Christmas pudding must be in a state of sacred isolation like an anchorite at prayer. I thought it meant that the presence of one's fellow creatures in some way disturbed the subtle nervous and digestive process through which Christmas pudding was beneficent. It sounded rather mad and wicked, certainly; but not madder or more wicked than many other things that I have read in scientific journals. But on re-reading the passage, I see that my first impression did the *Lancet* an injustice. The sentence really means that when one eats Christmas pudding one should eat nothing but Christmas pudding. 'It is,' says the *Lancet*, 'a complete meal in itself.' This is, I should say, a question of natural capacity, not to say of cubic capacity. I know a kind of person who would find one Christmas pudding a complete meal in itself, and even a little over. For my own part, I should say that three, or perhaps four, Christmas puddings might be said to constitute a complete meal in themselves. But, in any case, this sudden conversion of science to plum-pudding is a fine example of the fickleness of the human intellect and the steadiness of the human appetite. Scientific theories change, but the plum-pudding remains the same, century after century (I do not mean the individual pudding, but the type), a permanent monument of human mysticism and human mirth. If there is one thing more than another which from our childhood we have heard was grossly unwholesome and opposed to all medical advice, that thing certainly was Christmas pudding. Now it seems (again by the best medical advice) that to call Christmas pudding wholesome is entirely a faint and approximate expression of its merits. Not only is Christmas pudding wholesome, but it is so peculiarly and incomparably wholesome that no other and less medical substance must be taken with it so as to spoil its perfect medical effect. Who shall decide when doctors disagree—with themselves? The doctors will always disagree and humanity will always decide.

Literature has almost always failed in endeavouring to describe happiness as a state. Human tradition, human custom and folklore (though far more true and reliable than literature as a rule) have not often succeeded in giving quite the correct symbols for a real atmosphere of *camaraderie* and joy. But here and there the note has been struck with the sudden vibration of the *vox humana*. In human tradition it has been struck chiefly in the old celebrations of Christmas. In literature it has been struck chiefly in Dickens' Christmas tales.

In the historic celebration of Christmas as it remains from Catholic times in certain northern countries (and it is to be remembered that in Catholic times the northern countries were, if possible, more Catholic than anybody else) there are three qualities which explain, I think, its hold upon the human sense of happiness, especially in such men as Dickens. There are three notes of Christmas, so to speak, which are also notes of happiness, and which the pagans and the Utopians forget. If we state what they are in the case of Christmas, it will be quite sufficiently obvious how important they are in the case of Dickens.

The first quality is, I think, what may be called the dramatic quality. The happiness is not a state; it is a crisis. All the old customs surrounding the celebration of the birth of Christ are made by human instinct so as to insist and re-insist upon this crucial quality. Everything is so arranged that the whole household may feel, if possible, as a household does when a child is actually being born in it. The thing is a vigil and a vigil with a definite limit. People sit up at night until they hear the bells ring. Or they try to sleep at night in order to see their presents the next morning. Everywhere there is a limitation, a restraint; at one moment the door is shut, at the moment after it is opened. The hour has come or it has not come; the parcels are undone or they are not undone; there is no evolution of Christmas presents. This sharp and theatrical quality in pleasure, which human instinct and the mother wit of the world has wisely put into the popular celebrations of Christmas, is also a quality which is essential in such romantic literature as Dickens wrote. In romantic literature (that is, in permanent literature) the hero and heroine must indeed be happy, but they must also be unexpectedly happy. This is the first connecting link between literature and the old religious feast;

22

this is the first connecting link between Dickens and Christmas.

The second element to be found in all such festivity and all such romance is the element which is represented as well as it could be represented by the mere fact that Christmas occurs in the winter. It is the element not merely of contrast, but actually of antagonism. It preserves everything that was best in the merely primitive or pagan view of such ceremonies or such banquets. If we are carousing, at least we are warriors carousing. We hang above us, as it were, the shields and battle-axes with which we must do battle with the giants of the snow and hail. Man chooses when he wishes to be most joyful the very moment when the whole material universe is most sad. It is this contradiction and mystical defiance which gives a quality of manliness and reality to the old winter feasts which is not characteristic of the sunny felicities of the Earthly Paradise. And this curious element has been carried out even in all the trivial jokes and tasks that have always surrounded such occasions as these. The object of the jovial customs was not to make everything artificially easy; on the contrary, it was rather to make everything artificially difficult. The fundamental principle of idealism is not only expressed by shooting an arrow at the stars; the fundamental principle of idealism is also expressed by putting a leg of mutton at the top of a greasy pole. There is in all such observances a quality which can only be called the quality of divine obstruction. For instance, in the game of snapdragon (that admirable occupation) the conception is that raisins taste much nicer if they are brands saved from the burning. About all Christmas things there is something a little nobler, if only nobler in form and theory, than mere comfort; even holly is prickly.

It is not hard to see the connection of this kind of historic instinct with a romantic writer like Dickens. The healthy novelist must always play snapdragon with his principal characters; he must always be snatching the hero and heroine like raisins out of the fire. And though the third quality in Christmas is less obviously easy to explain its connection with Dickens, if it were explained it would be equally unimpeachable. The third great Christmas element is the element of the grotesque. The grotesque is the natural expression of joy; and all the Utopias and new Edens of the poets fail to give a real impression of enjoyment, very largely because they leave out the grotesque. A man in most modern Utopias cannot really be happy; he is too dignified. A man in Morris's Earthly Paradise cannot really be enjoying himself; he is too decorative. When real human beings have real delights they tend to express them entirely in grotesques—I might almost say entirely in goblins. On Christmas Eve one may talk about ghosts so long as they are turnip ghosts. One would not be allowed (I hope, in any decent family) to talk on Christmas Eve about astral bodies. The boar's head of old Yule-time was as grotesque as the donkey's head of Bottom the Weaver. But there are only one set of goblins quite wild enough to express the wild goodwill of Christmas. Those goblins are the characters of Dickens.

Arcadian poets and Arcadian painters have striven to express happiness by means of beautiful figures. Dickens understood that happiness is best expressed by ugly figures. In beauty, perhaps, there is something allied to sadness; certainly there is something akin to joy in the grotesque, nay, in the uncouth. There is something mysteriously associated with happiness not only in the corpulence of Falstaff and the corpulence of Tony Weller, but even in the red nose of Bardolph or the red nose of Mr Stiggins. A thing of beauty is an inspiration for ever—a matter of meditation for ever. It is rather a thing of ugliness that is strictly a joy for ever.

All these traits are generally characteristic of Dickens' works, but that is only because this Christmas atmosphere is generally characteristic of all his works. All his books are Christmas books. But these traits are still especially typical of the 'Christmas Books' properly so-called; his two or three famous Yuletide tales—'The Christmas Carol' and 'The Chimes' and 'The Cricket on the Hearth'. Of these 'The Christmas Carol' is beyond comparison the best as well as the most popular. Indeed, Dickens is in so profound and spiritual a sense a popular author that in his case, unlike most others, it can generally be said that the best work is the most popular. It is for 'Pickwick' that he is best known; and upon the whole it is for Pickwick that he is best worth knowing. In any case this superiority of 'The Christmas Carol' makes it convenient for us to take it as an example of the generalisations already made. If we study the very real atmosphere of rejoicing and of riotous charity in 'The Christmas Carol' we shall find that all the three marks I have mentioned are unmistakably visible. 'The Christmas Carol' is a happy story first, because it describes an abrupt and dramatic change; it is not only the story of a conversion, but of a sudden conversion; as sudden as the conversion of a man at a Salvation Army meeting. Popular religion is quite right in insisting on the fact of a crisis in most things. It is true that the man at the Salvation Army meeting would probably be converted from the punch bowl; whereas Scrooge was converted to it. That only means that Scrooge and Dickens represented a higher and more historic Christianity. But in both cases happiness is rightly valued because it follows dramatically upon unhappiness; happiness is valued because it is 'salvation'—something saved from the wreck.

Again, 'The Christmas Carol' owes much of its hilarity to our second source—the fact of its being a tale of winter and of a very wintry winter. There is much about comfort in the story; yet the comfort is never enervating: it is saved from that by a tingle of something bitter and bracing in the weather. Lastly, the story exemplifies throughout the power of the third principle—the kinship between gaiety and the grotesque. Everybody is happy because nobody is dignified. We have a feeling somehow that Scrooge looked even uglier when he was kind than he had looked when he was cruel. The turkey that Scrooge bought was so fat, says Dickens, that it could never have stood upright. That top-heavy and monstrous bird is a good symbol of the top-heavy happiness of the stories.

TURKEY

I do not know whether an animal killed at Christmas has had a better or a worse time than it would have had if there had been no Christmas or no Christmas dinners. But I do know that the fighting and suffering brotherhood to which I belong and owe everything, Mankind, would have a much worse time if there were no such thing as Christmas or Christmas dinners. Whether the turkey which Scrooge gave to Bob Cratchit had experienced a lovelier or more melancholy career than that of less attractive turkeys is a subject upon which I cannot even conjecture. But that Scrooge was better for giving the turkey and Cratchit happier for getting it I know as two facts, as I know that I have two feet. What life and death may be to a turkey is not my business; but the soul of Scrooge and the body of Cratchit are my business. Nothing shall induce me to darken human homes, to destroy human festivities, to insult human gifts and human benefactions for the sake of some hypothetical knowledge which Nature curtained from our eyes. We men and women are all in the same boat, upon a stormy sea.

We owe to each other a terrible and tragic loyalty. If we catch sharks for food, let them be killed most mercifully; let any one who likes love the sharks, and pet the sharks, and tie ribbons round their necks and give them sugar and teach them to dance. But if once a man suggests that a shark is to be valued against a sailor, or that the poor shark might be permitted to bite off a nigger's leg occasionally; then I would court-martial the man—he is a traitor to the ship.

Meanwhile, it remains true that I shall eat a great deal of turkey this Christmas; and it is not in the least true (as the vegetarians say) that I shall do it because I do not realise what I am doing, or because I do what I know is wrong, or that I do it with shame or doubt or a fundamental unrest of conscience. In one sense I know quite well what I am doing; in another sense I know quite well that I know not what I do. Scrooge and the Cratchits and I are, as I have said, all in one boat; the turkey and I are, to say the most of it, ships that pass in the night, and greet each other in passing. I wish him well; but it is really practically impossible to discover whether I treat him well. I can avoid, and I do avoid with horror, all special and artificial tormenting of him, sticking pins in him for fun or sticking knives in him for scientific investigation. But whether by feeding him slowly and killing him quickly for the needs of my brethren, I have improved in his own solemn eyes his own strange and separate destiny, whether I have made him in the sight of God a slave or a martyr, or one whom the gods love and who die young—that is far more removed from my possibilities of knowledge than the most abstruse intricacies of mysticism or theology. A turkey is more occult and awful than all the angels and archangels. In so far as God has partly revealed to us an angelic world, he has partly told us what an angel means. But God has never told us what a turkey means. And if you go and stare at a live turkey for an hour or two, you will find by the end of it that the enigma has rather increased than diminished.

MOCK TURKEY 🦃

I have before me a little pamphlet in which the most precise directions are given for a Mock Turkey, for a vegetarian mince-pie, and for a cautious and hygienic Christmas pudding. I have never quite understood why it should be a part of the Simple Life to have anything so deceptive and almost conspiratorial as an imitation turkey. The coarse and comic alderman may be expected, in his festive ribaldry, to mock a turtle; but surely a lean and earnest humanitarian ought not to mock a turkey. Nor do I understand the theory of the imitation in its relation to the ideal. Surely one who thinks meat-eating mere cannibalism ought not to arrange vegetables so as to look like an animal. It is as if a converted cannibal in the Sandwich Islands were to arrange joints of meat in the shape of a missionary. The missionaries would surely regard the proceedings of their convert with something less than approval, and perhaps with something akin to alarm.

SAUSAGES AND STARS ❧

The notion that the historic past, and particularly the Middle Ages, was a mass of negligible darkness, is pretty well gone by this time; and there are quite a large number of people engaged in collecting the original costumes, and the genuine ballads, and the authentic frying-pans of the twelfth century. The only thing that I never can understand about these people is why instead of admiring the doings of these ages, they do not merely do them. If ever there does appear a valid instance of these ancient observances continuing in actual operation at the present day, the antiquarians simply faint in the street at the sight of it. For example, most of my aesthetic friends lie awake at night dreaming of the reinstitution of some beautiful pagan festival, and yet none of them (for I have tempted them all) can eat four helpings of Christmas pudding. Christmas, with its sausages and its stars, is the very historic thing that they are talking about, but they resent it merely because it is still alive.

THE SHOP OF GHOSTS ❧

Nearly all the best and most precious things in the universe you can get for a halfpenny. I make an exception, of course, of the sun, the moon, the earth, people, stars, thunderstorms, and such trifles. You can get them for nothing. But the general principle will be at once apparent. In the street behind me, for instance, you can now get a ride on an electric tram for a halfpenny. To be on an electric tram is to be on a flying castle in a fairy tale. You can get quite a large number of brightly coloured sweets for a halfpenny.

But if you want to see what a vast and bewildering array of valuable things you can get at a halfpenny each, you should do as I was doing last night. I was gluing my nose against the glass of a very small and dimly lit toy shop in one of the greyest and leanest of the streets of Battersea. But dim as was that square of light, it was filled (as a child once said to me) with all the colours God ever made. Those toys of the poor were like the children who buy them; they were all dirty; but they were all bright. For my part, I think brightness more important than cleanliness; since the first is of the soul, and the second of the body. You must excuse me; I am a democrat; I know I am out of fashion in the modern world.

~   ~   ~

As I looked at that palace of pigmy wonders, at small green omnibuses, at small blue elephants, at small black dolls, and small red Noah's arks, I must have fallen into some sort of unnatural trance. That lit shop-window became like the brilliantly lit stage when one is watching some highly coloured comedy. I forgot the grey houses and the grimy people behind me as one forgets the dark galleries and the dim crowds at a theatre. It seemed as if the little objects behind the glass were small, not because they were toys, but because they were objects far away. The green omnibus was really a green omnibus, a green Bayswater omnibus, passing across some huge desert on its ordinary way to Bayswater. The blue elephant was no longer blue with paint; he was blue with distance. The black doll was really a negro relieved against passionate tropic foliage in the land where every weed is flaming and only man is black. The red Noah's ark was really the enormous ship of earthly salvation riding on the rain-swollen sea, red in the first morning of hope.

Every one, I suppose, knows such stunning instants of abstraction, such brilliant blanks in the mind. In such moments one can see the face of one's own best friend as an unmeaning pattern of spectacles or moustaches. They are commonly marked by the two signs of the slowness of their growth and the suddenness of their termination. The return to real thinking is often as abrupt as bumping into a man. Very often indeed (in my case) it is bumping into a man. But in any case the awakening is always emphatic and, generally speaking, it is always complete. Now, in this case, I did come back with a shock of sanity to the consciousness that I was, after all, only staring into a dingy little toy-shop; but in some strange way the mental cure did not seem to be final. There was still in my mind an unmanageable something that told me that I had strayed into some odd atmosphere, or that I had already done some odd thing. I felt as if I had worked a miracle or committed a sin. It was as if I had (at any rate) stepped across some border in the soul

To shake off this dangerous and dreamy sense I went into the shop and tried to buy wooden soldiers. The man in the shop was very old and broken, with confused white hair covering his head and half his face, hair so startlingly white that it looked almost artificial. Yet though he was senile and even sick, there was nothing of suffering in his eyes; he looked rather as if he were gradually falling asleep in a not unkindly decay. He gave me the wooden soldiers, but when I put down the money he did not at first seem to see it; then he blinked at it feebly, and then he pushed it feebly away.

'No, no,' he said vaguely. 'I never have. I never have. We are rather old-fashioned here.'

'Not taking money,' I replied, 'seems to me more like an uncommonly new fashion than an old one.'

'I never have,' said the old man, blinking and blowing his nose; 'I've always given presents. I'm too old to stop.'

'Good heavens!' I said. 'What can you mean? Why, you might be Father Christmas.'

'I am Father Christmas,' he said apologetically, and blew his nose again.

The lamps could not have been lighted yet in the street outside. At any rate, I could see nothing against the darkness but the shining shop-window. There were no sounds of steps or voices in the street; I might have strayed into some new and sunless world. But something had cut the cords of common sense, and I could not feel even surprise except sleepily. Something made me say, 'You look ill, Father Christmas.'

'I am dying,' he said.

I did not speak, and it was he who spoke again.

'All the new people have left my shop. I cannot understand it. They seem to object to me on such curious and inconsistent sort of grounds, these scientific men, and these innovators. They say that

I give people superstitions and make them too visionary; they say I give people sausages and make them too coarse. They say my heavenly parts are too heavenly; they say my earthly parts are too earthly; I don't know what they want, I'm sure. How can heavenly things be too heavenly, or earthly things too earthly? How can one be too good, or too jolly? I don't understand. But I understand one thing well enough. These modern people are living and I am dead.'

'You may be dead,' I replied. 'You ought to know. But as for what they are doing—do not call it living.'

❧ ❧ ❧

A silence fell suddenly between us which I somehow expected to be unbroken. But it had not fallen for more than a few seconds when, in the utter stillness, I distinctly heard a very rapid step coming nearer and nearer along the street. The next moment a figure flung itself into the shop and stood framed in the doorway. He wore a large white hat tilted back as if in impatience; he had tight bright old-fashioned pantaloons, a gaudy old-fashioned stock and waistcoat, and an old fantastic coat. He had large wide-open luminous eyes like those of an arresting actor; he had a fiery, nervous face, and a fringe of beard. He took in the shop and the old man in a look that seemed literally a flash and uttered the exclamation of a man utterly staggered.

'Good lord!' he cried out; 'it can't be you! It isn't you! I came to ask where your grave was.'

'I'm not dead yet, Mr Dickens,' said the old gentleman, with a feeble smile; 'but I'm dying,' he hastened to add reassuringly.

'But, dash it all, you were dying in my time,' said Mr Charles Dickens with animation; 'and you don't look a day older.'

'I've felt like this for a long time,' said Father Christmas.

Mr Dickens turned his back and put his head out of the door into the darkness.

'Dick,' he roared at the top of his voice; 'he's still alive.'

❧ ❧ ❧

Another shadow darkened the doorway, and a much larger and more full-blooded gentleman in an enormous periwig came in, fanning his flushed face with a military hat of the cut of Queen

30

Anne. He carried his head well back like a soldier, and his hot face had even a look of arrogance, which was suddenly contradicted by his eyes, which were literally as humble as a dog's. His sword made a great clatter, as if the shop were too small for it.

'Indeed,' said Sir Richard Steele, ''tis a most prodigious matter, for the man was dying when we wrote about Sir Roger de Coverley and his Christmas Day.'

My senses were growing dimmer and the room darker. It seemed to be filled with new-comers.

'It hath ever been understood,' said a burly man, who carried his head humorously and obstinately a little on one side—I think he was Ben Jonson—'It hath ever been understood, consule Jacobo, under our King James and her late Majesty, that such good and hearty customs were fallen sick, and like to pass from the world. This grey beard most surely was no lustier when I knew him than now.'

And I also thought I heard a green-clad man, like Robin Hood, say in some mixed Norman French, 'But I saw the man dying'.

'I have felt like this a long time,' said Father Christmas, in his feeble way again.

Mr Charles Dickens suddenly leant across to him.

'Since when?' he asked. 'Since you were born?'

'Yes,' said the old man, and sank shaking into a chair. 'I have been always dying.'

Mr Dickens took off his hat with a flourish like a man calling a mob to rise.

'I understand it now,' he cried, 'you will never die.'

III
The Inn at the
End of the World

POEMS OF MIDDLE LIFE, 1900-1914

A CHILD OF THE SNOWS ❦

There is heard a hymn when the panes are dim,
    And never before or again,
When the nights are strong with a darkness long,
    And the dark is alive with rain.

Never we know but in sleet and in snow,
    The place where the great fires are,
That the midst of the earth is a raging mirth
    And the heart of the earth a star.

And at night we win to the ancient inn
    Where the child in the frost is furled,
We follow the feet where all souls meets
    At the inn at the end of the world.

The gods lie dead where the leaves lie red,
    For the flame of the sun is flown,
The gods lie cold where the leaves lie gold,
    And a Child comes forth alone.

THE HOUSE OF CHRISTMAS ❦

There fared a mother driven forth
Out of an inn to roam;
In the place where she was homeless
All men are at home.
The crazy stable close at hand,
With shaking timber and shifting sand,
Grew a stronger thing to abide and stand
Than the square stones of Rome.

For men are homesick in their homes,
And strangers under the sun,
And they lay their heads in a foreign land
Whenever the day is done.
Here we have battle and blazing eyes,
And chance and honour and high surprise,

But our homes are under miraculous skies
Where the yule tale was begun.

A Child in a foul stable,
Where the beasts feed and foam;
Only where He was homeless
Are you and I at home;
We have hands that fashion and heads that know,
But our hearts we lost—how long ago!
In a place no chart nor ship can show
Under the sky's dome.

This world is wild as an old wives' tale,
And strange the plain things are,
The earth is enough and the air is enough
For our wonder and our war;
But our rest is as far as the fire-drake swings
And our peace is put in impossible things
Where clashed and thundered unthinkable wings
Round an incredible star.

To an open house in the evening
Home shall men come,
To an older place than Eden
And a taller town than Rome.
To the end of the way of the wandering star,
To the things that cannot be and that are,
To the place where God was homeless
And all men are at home.

A WORD ❧

A word came forth in Galilee, a word like to a star;
It climbed and rang and blessed and burnt wherever brave
    hearts are;
A word of sudden secret hope, of trial and increase
Of wrath and pity fused in fire, and passion kissing peace.
A star that o'er the citied world beckoned, a sword of flame;
A star with myriad thunders tongued: a mighty word there
    came.

The wedge's dart passed into it, the groan of timber wains,
The ringing of the rivet nails, the shrieking of the planes;
The hammering on the roofs at morn, the busy workshop
     roar;
The hiss of shavings drifted deep along the windy floor;
The heat-browned toiler's crooning song, the hum of human
     worth
Mingled of all the noise of crafts, the ringing word went forth.

The splash of nets passed into it, the grind of sand and shell,
The boat-hook's clash, the boat-oars' jar, the cries to buy and
     sell,
The flapping of the landed shoals, the canvas crackling free,
And through all varied notes and cries, the roaring of the sea,
The noise of little lives and brave, of needy lives and high;
In gathering all the throes of earth, the living word went by.

Earth's giant sins bowed down to it, in Empire's huge eclipse,
When darkness sat above the thrones, seven thunders on her
     lips,
The woes of cities entered it, the clang of idols' falls,
The scream of filthy Caesars stabbed high in their brazen halls,
The dim hoarse floods of naked men, the world-realms'
     snapping girth,
The trumpets of Apocalypse, the darkness of the earth:

The wrath that brake the eternal lamp and hid the eternal hill,
A world's destruction loading, the word went onward still—
The blaze of creeds passed into it, the hiss of horrid fires,
The headlong spear, the scarlet cross, the hair-shirt and the
     briars,
The cloistered brethren's thunderous chaunt, the errant
     champion's song,
The shifting of the crowns and thrones, the tangle of the
     strong.

The shattering fall of crest and crown and shield and cross and
     cope,
The tearing of the gauds of time, the blight of prince and
     pope,
The reign of ragged millions leagued to wrench a loaded debt,

Loud with the many throated roar, the word went forward
    yet.
The song of wheels passed into it, the roaring and the smoke
The riddle of the want and wage, the fogs that burn and
    choke.

The breaking of the girths of gold, the needs that creep and
    swell,
The strengthening hope, the dazing light, the deafening
    evangel,
Through kingdoms dead and empires damned, through
    changes without cease,
With earthquake, chaos, born and fed, rose,—and the word
    was 'Peace'.

THE TRUCE OF CHRISTMAS 🐟

Passionate peace is in the sky—
And in the snow in silver sealed
The beasts are perfect in the field,
And men seem men so suddenly—
   (But take ten swords and ten times ten
   And blow the bugle in praising men;
   For we are for all men under the sun;
   And they are against us every one;
   And misers haggle and madmen clutch,
   And there is peril in praising much,
   And we have the terrible tongues uncurled
   That praise the world to the sons of the world.)

The idle humble hill and wood
Are bowed upon the sacred birth,
And for one little hour the earth
Is lazy with the love of good—
   (But ready are you, and ready am I,
   If the battle blow and the guns go by;
   For we are for all men under the sun,
   And they are against us every one;

And the men that hate herd all together,
To pride and gold, and the great white feather,
And the thing is graven in star and stone
That the men who love are all alone.)

Hunger is hard and time is tough,
But bless the beggars and kiss the kings;
For hope has broken the heart of things,
And nothing was ever praised enough.
   (But hold the shield for a sudden swing
   And point the sword when you praise a thing,
   For we are for all men under the sun,
   And they are against us every one;
   And mime and merchant, thane and thrall
   Hate us because we love them all;
   Only till Christmastide go by
   Passionate peace is in the sky.)

A SONG OF GIFTS TO GOD ❧

When the first Christmas presents came, the straw where
   Christ was rolled
Smelt sweeter than their frankincense, burnt brighter than their
   gold,
And a wise man said, 'We will not give; the thanks would be
   but cold.'

'Nay,' said the next. 'To all new gifts, to this gift or another,
Bends the high gratitude of God; even as He now, my
   brother,
Who had a Father for all time, yet thanks Him for a Mother.

'Yet scarce for Him this yellow stone or prickly smells and
   sparse,
Who holds the gold heart of the sun that fed these timber
   bars,
Nor any scentless lily lives for One that smells the stars.'

Then spake the third of the Wise Men, the wisest of the three:
'We may not with the widest lives enlarge His liberty,
Whose wings are wider than the world. It is not He, but we.

'We say not He has more to gain, but we have more to lose.
Less gold shall go astray, we say, less gold, if thus we choose,
Go to make harlots of the Greeks and hucksters of the Jews.

'Less clouds before colossal feet redden in the underlight,
To the blind gods from Babylon less incense burn to-night,
To the high beasts of Babylon, whose mouths make mock of
        right.'

Babe of the thousand birthdays, we that are young yet grey,
White with the centuries, still can find no better thing to say,
We that with sects and whims and wars have wasted
        Christmas Day.

Light Thou Thy censer, to Thyself, for all our fires are dim,
Stamp Thou Thine image on our coins, for Caesar's face grows
        grim,
And a dumb devil of pride and greed has taken hold of him.

We bring Thee back great Christendom, churches and towns
        and towers,
And if our hands are glad, O God, to cast them down like
        flowers,
'Tis not that they enrich Thine hands, but they are saved from
        ours.

IV
A Feast of Fools
ESSAYS, COMMENT AND A STORY

Most sensible people say that adults cannot be expected to appreciate Christmas as much as children appreciate it. At least, Mr G. S. Street said so, who is the most sensible man now writing in the English language. But I am not sure that even sensible people are always right; and this has been my principal reason for deciding to be silly—a decision that is now irrevocable. It may be only because I am silly, but I rather think that, relatively to the rest of the year, I enjoy Christmas more than I did when I was a child. Of course, children do enjoy Christmas—they enjoy almost everything except actually being smacked: from which truth the custom no doubt arose. But the real point is not whether a schoolboy would enjoy Christmas. The point is that he would also enjoy No Christmas. Now I say most emphatically that I should denounce, detest, abominate, and abjure the insolent institution of No Christmas. The child is glad to find a new ball, let us say, which Uncle William (dressed as St Nicholas in everything except the halo) has put in his stocking. But if he had no new ball, he would make a hundred new balls out of the snow. And for them he would be indebted not to Christmas, but to winter. I suppose snowballing is being put down by the police, like every other Christian custom. No more will a prosperous and serious City man have a large silver star splashed suddenly on his waistcoat, veritably investing him with the Order of the Star of Bethlehem. For it is the star of innocence and novelty, and should remind him that a child can still be born. But indeed, in one sense, we may truly say the children enjoy no seasons, because they enjoy all. I myself am of the physical type that greatly prefers cold weather to hot; and I could more easily believe that Eden was at the North Pole than anywhere in the Tropics. It is hard to define the effect of weather: I can only say that all the rest of the year I am untidy, but in summer I feel untidy. Yet although (according to the modern biologists) my hereditary human body must have been of the same essential type in my boyhood as in my present decrepitude, I can distinctly remember hailing the idea of freedom and even energy on days that were quite horribly hot. It was the excellent custom at my school to give the boys a half-holiday when it seemed too hot for working. And I can well remember the gigantic joy with which I left off reading Virgil and began to run round and round a field. My tastes in this matter have changed. Nay, they have been reversed. If I now found myself (by some process I cannot easily conjecture) on a burning summer day running round and round a field, I hope I shall not appear pedantic if I say I should prefer to be reading Virgil.

And thus it is really possible, from one point of view, for elderly gentlemen to frolic at Christmas more than children can. They may really come to find Christmas more entertaining, as they have come to find Virgil more entertaining. And, in spite of all the talk about the coldness of classicism, the poet who wrote about the man who in his own country home fears neither King nor crowd was not by any means incapable of understanding Mr Wardle. And it is exactly those sentiments, and similar ones, that the adult does appreciate better than the child. The adult, for instance, appreciates domesticity better than the child. And one of the pillars and first principles of domesticity, as Mr Belloc has rightly pointed out, is the institution of private property. The Christmas pudding represents the mature mystery of property; and the proof of it is in the eating.

I have always held that Peter Pan was wrong. He was a charming boy, and sincere in his adventurousness; but though he was brave like a boy, he was also a coward—like a boy. He admitted it would be a great adventure to die; but it did not seem to occur to him that it would be a great adventure to live. If he had consented to march with the fraternity of his fellow-creatures, he would have found that there were solid experiences and important revelations even in growing up. They are realities which could not possibly have been made real to him without wrecking the real good in his own juvenile point of view. But that is exactly why he ought to have done as he was told. That is the only argument for authority. In dealing with childhood, we have a parental right to command it—because we should kill the childhood if we convinced it.

Now the mistake of Peter Pan is the mistake of the new theory of life. I might call it Peter Pantheism. It is the notion that there is *no* advantage in striking root. Yet, if you talk intelligently to the nearest tree, the tree will tell you that you are an unobservant ass. There is an advantage in root; and the name of it is fruit. It is not true that the nomad is even freer than the peasant. The Bedouin may rush past on his camel, leaving a whirl of dust; but dust is not free because it flies. Neither is the nomad free because he flies. You cannot grow cabbages on a camel, any more than in a condemned cell. Moreover, I believe camels commonly walk in a comparatively leisurely manner. Anyhow, most merely nomadic creatures do, for it is a great nuisance to 'carry one's house with one'. Gipsies do it; so do snails; but neither of them travel very fast. I inhabit one of the smallest houses that can be conceived by the cultivated classes; but I frankly confess I should be sorry to carry it with me whenever I went out for a walk. It is true that some motorists almost live in their motor-cars. But it gratifies me to state that these motorists generally die in their motor-cars too. They perish, I am pleased to say, in a startling and horrible manner, as a judgment on them for trying to outstrip creatures higher than themselves—such as the gipsy and the snail. But, broadly speaking, a house is a thing that stands still. And a thing that stands still is a thing that strikes root. One of the things that strike root is Christmas: and another is middle-age. The other great pillar of private life besides property is marriage; but I will not deal with it here. Suppose a man has neither wife nor child: suppose he has only a good servant, or only a small garden, or only a small house, or only a small dog. He will still find he has struck unintentional root. He realizes there is something in his own garden that was not even in the Garden of Eden; and therefore is not (I kiss my hand to the Socialists) in Kew Gardens or in Kensington Gardens. He realizes, what Peter Pan could not be made to realize, that a plain human house of one's own, standing in one's own backyard, is really quite as romantic as a rather cloudy house at the top of a tree or a highly conspiratorial house underneath the roots of it. But this is because he has explored his own house, which Peter Pan and such discontented children seldom do. All the same, the children ought to think of the Never-Never Land—the world that is outside. But we ought to think of the Ever-Ever Land—the world which is inside, and the world which will last. And that is why, wicked as we are, we know most about Christmas.

DICKENS AGAIN ✒

I am sorry that the comic costume festival which was organised for Christmas by one of the chief Dickensian societies has unavoidably fallen through. It is not for me to reproach those traitors who found it impossible to turn up: for I was one of those traitors myself. Whatever character it was that I was expected to appear in—Jingle, I suppose, or possibly Uriah Heep—was, under a final press of business, refused by me. These Dickensian enthusiasts were going to have a Christmas party at Rochester, where they would brew punch and drink punch, and drive coaches and fall off coaches, and do all the proper Pickwickian things. How many of them were ready to make a hole in the ice, to be wheeled about in a wheelbarrow, or to wait all night outside a ladies' school, the official documents have not informed me. But I would gladly take a moderate part. I could not brew punch for the Pickwick Club; but I could drink it. I could not drive the coach for the Pickwick Club—or, indeed, for any club except the Suicide Club; but I could fall off the coach amid repeated applause and enthusiastic encores. I should be only too proud if it could be said of me, as of Sam's hyperbolical old gentleman who was tipped into the hyperbolical canal, that "is 'at was found, but I can't be certain 'is 'ead was in it'. It seems to me like a euthanasia: more beautiful than the passing of Arthur.

But though the failure of this particular festivity was merely accidental (like my own unfortunate fall off the coach), it is not without its parallel in the present position of Dickensians and Christmas. For the truth is that we simply cannot recreate the Pickwick Club—unless we have a moral basis as sturdy as that of Dickens, and even a religious basis as sturdy as that of Christmas. Men at such a time turn their backs to the solemn thing they are celebrating, as the horses turn their backs to the coach. But they are pulling the coach. And the best of it is this: that so long as the Christmas feast had some kind of assumed and admitted meaning, it was praised, and praised sympathetically, by the great men whom we should call most unsympathetic with it. That Shakespeare and Dickens and Walter Scott should write of it seems quite natural. They were people who would be as welcome at Christmas as Santa Claus. But I do not think many people have ever wished they could ask Milton to eat the Christmas pudding. Nevertheless, it is quite certain that his Christmas ode is not only one of the richest but one of the most human of his masterpieces. I do not think that anyone specially wanting a rollicking article on Christmas would desire, by mere instinct, the literary style of Addison. Yet it is quite certain that the somewhat difficult task of really liking Addison is rendered easier by his account of the Coverley Christmas than by anything else he wrote. I even go so far as to doubt whether one of the little Cratchits (who stuffed their spoons in their mouths lest they should scream for goose) would have removed the spoon to say, 'Oh, that Tennyson were here!' Yet certainly Tennyson's spirits do seem to revive in a more or less real way at the ringing of the Christmas bells in the most melancholy part of *In Memoriam*. These great men were not trying to be merry: some of them, indeed, were trying to be miserable. But the day itself was too strong for them; the time was more than their temperaments; the tradition was alive. The festival was roaring in the streets, so that prigs and even prophets (who are sometimes worse still) were honestly carried off their feet.

The difficulty with Dickens is not any failure in Dickens, nor even in the popularity of Dickens. On the contrary, he has recaptured his creative reputation and fascination far more than any of the other great Victorians. Macaulay, who was really great in his way, is rejected; Cobbett, who was much greater, is forgotten. Dickens is not merely alive: he is risen from the dead. But the difficulty is in the failing under his feet, as it were, of that firm historic platform on which he had performed his Christmas pantomimes: a platform of which he was quite as unconscious as we, most of us, are of the floor we walk about on. The fact is that the fun of Christmas is founded on the seriousness of Christmas; and to pull away the latter support even from under a Christmas clown is to let him down through a trap-door. And even clowns do not like the trap-doors that they do not expect. Thus it is unfortunately true that so glorious a thing as a Pickwick party tends to lose the splendid quality of a mere Mummery, and become that much more dull and conventional thing, a Covent Garden Ball. We are not ourselves living in the proper spirit of Pickwick. We are pretending to be old Dickens characters, when we ought to be new Dickens characters in reality.

The conditions are further complicated by the fact that while reading Dickens may make a man Dickensian, studying Dickens makes him quite the reverse. One might as well expect the aged custodian of a museum of sculpture to look (and dress) like the Apollo Belvedere, as expect the Pickwickian qualities in those literary critics who are attracted by the Dickens fiction as the materials for a biography or the subject of a controversy; as a mass of detail; as a record and a riddle. Those who study such things are a most valuable class of the community, and they do good service to Dickens in their own way. But their type and temperament are not, in the nature of things, likely to be full of the festive magic of their master. Take, for example, these endless discussions about the proper ending of *Edwin Drood*. I thought Mr William Archer's contributions to the query some time ago were particularly able and interesting; but I could not, with my hand on my heart, call Mr William Archer a festive gentleman, or one supremely fitted to follow Mr Swiveller as Perpetual Grand of the Glorious Apollos. Or again, I see that Sir William Robertson Nicoll has been writing on the same Drood mystery; and I know that his knowledge of Victorian literature is both vast and exact. But I hardly think that a Puritan Scot with a sharp individualistic philosophy would be the right person to fall off the coach. Sir William Nicoll, if I remember right, once forcibly described his individualist philosophy as 'firing out the fools'. And certainly the spirit of Dickens could be best described as the delight in firing them in. It is exactly because Christmas is not only a feast of children, but in some sense a feast of fools, that Dickens is in touch with its mystery.

A CHRISTMAS PRESENT 🖎

A person of great generosity has given me for a Christmas present an enormous resplendent walking-stick—with silver bands, a shiny handle, and all sorts of things I had never heard of. Its splendour, indeed, creates a kind of problem. The walking-stick and I do not suit each other. The only question is, which shall give way? May it not reasonably be supposed that after a few days in my company the walking-stick may take on a more dingy, battered, and comfortable look? Or must I dress up to the walking-stick? In the fairy tales (on which I rely more and more) the touch of a wand can turn the Beast into a beautiful Prince. Perhaps the touch of this stick can turn the beast now under discussion into a beautiful dandy. Already I feel vaguely that I ought to have one neat kid glove with which to hold the stick. From this it is but a step to having good cuffs and shirt-links, and so the creeping paralysis of propriety may crawl up my arms and cover my whole person. In a year or so the stick may have transformed me wholly into its own image. Whether this will ever happen I do not know. What I do know is that if I walk down the streets with the stick at present most people mistake me for a tramp who has stolen a gentleman's walking-stick.

After earnest thought, prayer, and meditation, I have come to the conclusion that it is my destiny in life to be a foil to the stick. I am only a background—a gloomy, a rugged background—against which the stick picks itself out in sparkling purity and distinctness. I suppose the strict grammatical definition of a walking-stick is a stick that can walk. I am sure this stick can walk by itself; I am merely a large, a florid tassle attached to it. The people of Battersea will merely praise the stick as they see it passing along the street. Then, when their admiration of it is exhausted (if that be conceivable) they may add: 'And how artistic an idea to tie on to this walking-stick an ill-dressed and unattractive human being, thus celebrating supremely and in an image the victory of the inanimate over the animate.' I exist only in order to throw up the high light upon the lustrous stick. What matters it that I am abased so long as It is exalted. At any rate, this simple resolution to be a background to the stick is much less terrible than the other idea of living up to it.

THE THEOLOGY OF CHRISTMAS PRESENTS ❧

Those modern theologians who insist that Christianity is not in doctrines, but in spirit, commonly fail to notice that they are exposing themselves to a test more abrupt and severe than that of doctrine itself. Some legal preliminaries at least are necessary before a man can be burned for his opinions; but without any preliminaries at all a man can be shot for his tone of voice. The old-fashioned Christian may be even more rapid in his decision that certain new views are unsympathetic than in his decision that they are unorthodox. It is much easier to detect and dislike the smell of a heresy than to trace it to its chemical ingredients. And when the new theologian throws over history and exact metaphysics, and simply says: 'Stripped of its formalities, this is Christianity,' he lies more open than the old theologian to the purely personal answer of the man in the street, 'If that is Christianity, take it away.'

One may consider gunpowder as a thing composed of charcoal, sulphur and saltpetre: or one may consider gunpowder (as does the more direct intellect of the maiden aunt) as a thing that ends in a bang. But if the philosopher of innovation boasts of bringing no salt, sulphur or charcoal, we do expect at least a bang, and a good

48

one. If he can blow up Parliament with milk, salad oil and fine sawdust, let him. But Parliament must be blown up; that, we shall all agree, is the essential. Now Christianity, whatever else it is, is an explosion. Whether or no it consists of the Fall, the Incarnation, the Resurrection, it does certainly consist of thunder, of prodigy, and of fire. Unless it is sensational there is simply no sense in it. Unless the Gospel sounds like a gun going off it has not been uttered at all. And if the new theologies sound like steam slowly escaping from a leaky kettle, then even the untrained ear of the ordinary layman (who knows neither chemistry nor theology) can detect the difference between that sound and an explosion. It is vain for such reformers to say that they go, not by the letter, but by the spirit. For they are even more plainly opposed to the spirit than they are to the letter.

Let us take one instance out of many of this principle in operation; the case of Christmas presents. A little while ago I saw a statement by Mrs Eddy on this subject, in which she said that she did not give presents in a gross, sensuous, terrestrial sense, but sat still and thought about Truth and Purity till all her friends were much better for it. Now I do not say that this plan is either superstitious or impossible, and no doubt it has an economic charm. I say it is un-Christian in the same solid and prosaic sense that playing a tune backwards is unmusical or saying 'ain't' is ungrammatical. I do not know that there is any Scriptural text or Church Council that condemns Mrs Eddy's theory of Christmas presents: but Christianity condemns it, as soldiering condemns running away. The two attitudes are antagonistic not only in their theology, not only in their thought, but in their state of soul before they ever begin to think. The idea of embodying goodwill—that is, of putting it into a body—is the huge and primal idea of the Incarnation. A gift of God that can be seen and touched is the whole point of the epigram of the creed. Christ Himself was a Christmas present. The note of material Christmas presents is struck even before He is born in the first movements of the sages and the star. The Three Kings came to Bethlehem bringing gold and frankincense and myrrh. If they had only brought Truth and Purity and Love there would have been no Christian art and no Christian civilisation.

Many sermons must have been preached upon those three gifts; but there is one aspect of them that has hardly received due attention. It is odd that our European sceptics, while borrowing from Oriental philosophers so much of their determinism and their despair, are perpetually sneering at the one Oriental element which Christianity eagerly incorporated, the one Oriental element which is really simple and delightful. I mean the Oriental love of gay colours and an infantile excitement about luxury. Sceptic after sceptic has called the New Jerusalem of St John a lump of vulgar jewellery. Sceptic after sceptic has denounced the rites of the Church as parades of sensual purple and tawdry gold. But in this selection, indeed, the Church was wiser than either Europe or Asia. She saw that the Eastern appetite for scarlet and silver and gold and green was in itself innocent and ardent, though wasted by the lower civilisations upon the pampering of idleness and tyranny. She saw that the stoic plainness of the Roman had in it a peril of stiffness and pride, though this was allied with the equality and public spirit of the highest civilisation then extant. The Church took all the labyrinthine gold and crawling colours which had adorned so many erotic poems and cruel romances in the East, and she lit those motley flames to illuminate gigantic humility and the greater intensities of innocence. She took the colours from the serpent's back: but she left the serpent. The European peoples have, upon the whole, followed in this the lead of Christian instinct and Christian art. Nothing is healthier in our popular tradition than the fact that we regard the East as a mass of quaint shapes and colours rather than a rival philosophical system. Though it is in fact a temple of hoary cosmologies, we treat it as a big bazaar—that is, as an enormous toy-shop. The real people remember the Near East, not by the Arabian prophet, but by the 'Arabian Nights'. Constantinople was captured by a Saracen culture scarce inferior, at the time, to ours. But we do not trouble about Turkish culture, but rather about Turkey carpets. The Celestial Empire has been filled for ages with an ironical agnosticism. But we Europeans do not ask for Chinese enigmas, but rather for Chinese puzzles. We regard the East as a great Gamage's; and we do well. This is the heartiest and most human thing in the East, what is called the violence of its colouring and the vulgarity of its gems. How evil are other Eastern things, the wheels of mental destiny and the wastes of mental doubt, we can only know from the modern sceptics themselves, who give us the dreary Eastern attitude combined with the dreary Western costume. Schopenhauer shows us the poison of the snake without its glitter, as the early Church showed us the glitter without the poison. It was the glitter that Christendom took out of the tangle of Eastern things. Gold ran like fire in a forest round every script and statute, and clung to the head of every king and saint. But it all came from the one lump of gold that Melchior bore in his hand when he went across deserts to Bethlehem.

The other two gifts are marked even more by the great Christian note—the note of the sensuous and the material. There is even something brazenly carnal about the appeal to the sense of smell in frankincense and myrrh. The nose is not left out of the divine human body. An organ which to the modern mind seems as comic as an elephant's trunk is familiarly recognised in such Oriental imagery. But, to insist on the other side in turn, this Asiatic luxury is in the Christian mystery only admitted in order to be subordinate to a higher simplicity and sanity. The gold is brought to a stable; the kings go seeking a carpenter. The wise men are on the march, not to find wisdom, but rather a strong and sacred ignorance. The wise men came from the East; but they went Westward to find God.

Besides this bodily and incarnate quality which makes Christmas presents so Christian, there is another element with a similar spiritual effect: I mean what may be called their particularism. On this, again, the new theories (of which Christian science is the largest and most lucid) strike a note startlingly dissimilar and opposite. Modern theology will tell us that the Child of Bethlehem is only an abstraction of all children; that the mother from Nazareth is a metaphysical symbol of motherhood. The truth is that it is only because the Nativity is a narrative of one lonely and literal mother and child that it is universal at all. If Bethlehem were not particular it would not be popular. In the same way a love-song to a scornful woman might be so piercing and mortal that all men sang it morn and eve, the hind at the plough and the prince in the saddle. But they would all stop singing suddenly if you told them that the song was not made about one woman, but only about women in the abstract. Christmas, down to its most homely and even comic observances of stockings and boxes, is penetrated with this personal idea of a secret between God and man—a divine cap that fits the particular human head. The cosmos is conceived as a central and celestial post-office. The postal system is, indeed, vast and rapid, but the parcels are all addressed, sealed and inviolate. A pillar-box is only public in order that a letter may be private. Christmas presents are a standing protest on behalf of giving as distinct from that mere sharing that modern moralities offer as equivalent or superior. Christmas stands for this superb and sacred paradox: that it is a higher spiritual transaction for Tommy and Molly each to give each other sixpence than for both equally to share a shilling. Christmas is something better than a thing for all; it is a thing for everybody. And if anyone finds such phrases aimless or fantastic, or thinks that the distinction has no existence except in a refinement of words, the only test is that I have indicated already—the permanent test of the populace. Take any hundred girls from a board school and see whether they do not make a distinction between a flower for each and a garden for all. If therefore new spiritual schools are concerned to prove that they have the spirit and secret of the Christian festival, they must prove it, not by abstract affirmations, but by things that have a special and unmistakable smack, by hitting one pungent tinge of taste, by being able to write a Christmas carol, or even to make a Christmas pie.

CHRISTMAS AND THE PROFESSORS ❧

There is one very vile habit that the pedants have, and that is explaining to a man why he does a thing which the man himself can explain quite well—and quite differently. If I go down on all-fours to find sixpence, it annoys me to be told by a passing biologist that I am really doing it because my remote ancestors were quadrupeds. I concede that he knows all about biology, or even a great deal about my ancestors; but I know he is wrong, because he does not know about the sixpence. If I climb a tree after a stray cat, I am unconvinced when a stray anthropologist tells me that I am doing it because I am essentially arboreal and barbaric. I happen to know why I am doing it; and I know it is because I am amiable and somewhat over-civilised. Scientists will talk to a man on general guess-work about things that they know no more about than about his pocket-money or his pet cat. Religion is one of them, and all the festivals and formalities that are rooted in religion. Thus a man will tell me that in keeping Christmas I am not keeping a Christian feast, but a pagan feast. This is exactly as if he told me that I was not feeling furiously angry, but only a little sad. I know how I am feeling all right; and why I am feeling it. I know this in the case of cats, sixpences, anger, and Christmas Day. When a learned man tells me that on the 25th of December I am really astronomically worshipping the sun, I answer that I am not. I am practising a particular personal religion, the pleasures of which (right or wrong) are not in the least astronomical. If he says that the cult of Christmas and the cult of Apollo are the same, I answer that they are utterly different; and I ought to know, for I have held both of them. I believed in Apollo when I was quite little; and I believe in Christmas now that I am very, very big.

Let us not take with such smooth surrender these tenth-truths at tenth hand, such as the phrase that Christmas is pagan in origin. Let us note exactly how much it really means. It amounts, so far as our knowledge goes, solely to this—that primitive Scandinavians did hold a feast in mid-winter. What the dickens else could primitive Scandinavians do, especially in winter? That they put on the largest log in winter: do the professors expect such simple pagans to put on the largest log in summer? It amounts to this, again—that many tribes have either worshipped the sun or (more probably) compared some god or hero to the sun. Just so many a poet has compared his lady to the sun—without by any means intending that she was a Solar Myth. Thus, by talking a great deal about the solar solstice, it can be maintained that Christmas is a sort of sun-worship; to all of which the simple answer is that it feels quite different. If people profess to feel 'the spirit' behind symbols, the first thing I expect of them is that they shall feel how opposite are the adoration of the sun and the following of the star.

SOME FALLACIES AND SANTA CLAUS ✑

Intelligent children, whether they believed or not in the sacred and benevolent burglary every Christmas Eve, would feel that the magi, the saint, the heathen god, etc., did not really make up the image of the old man with the furred coat and the reindeers: or if they did not feel so, they would have developed their intelligence at the ruinous expense of their childhood. But, indeed, in such cases, childhood and intelligence fail together. There are three or four films or veils of peculiarly modern ignorance which make the true statement of such popular 'extra-belief' very difficult. The first is that men in our restless capitalist society cannot understand that tradition, if it exists at all, is always much fresher and more forcible than anything else; the second thing not understood is that agnosticism cuts both ways; the third is that even the credulity of the populace has generally been a creative credulity of their own, not a mere gaping acceptance of sacerdotal conjuring tricks; the fourth is that the religious really domesticate their deities; and the fifth is that, in things of the imagination, unlike things of reason, the form is the spirit.

To apply these few tests very briefly in their order is perhaps the best way of blocking in the main realities about so popular yet so mysterious a figure. The point about tradition is this; that it is only called antiquated, nay, it is only thought of as old, when it does not exist at all. Certain ladies have probably painted their faces red ever since the ancient Britons painted their faces blue; but we do not think of the red paint as old, because it has been successfully handed on; it is a real tradition. We think of the blue paint as old because it has not been handed on, and is not a tradition. Now, whenever tradition is thus present at all, it must be more vivid and convincing than any records or theories; and this is obviously so in the case of the Christmas legend. Suppose somebody tried to persuade you or me that there had been no such thing as a Christmas festivity and excitement in the time of our grandfathers or great-grandfathers. It would be totally useless for them to tell us that letters had come to light showing that a non-existent ceremony had been invented as a practical joke on Washington Irving, as an American; that in the original manuscript in the British Museum Dickens wrote 'A Candlemas Carol', and that it is altered in a later hand to 'A Christmas Carol'; that Sir Roger de Coverley and his Christmas is a forgery written a short time ago by Mr Bernard Shaw; that Grimaldi with his dying breath had declared that he acted in pantomimes towards the end of December solely out of respect for the stoning of St Stephen; or any number of such detailed alterations. We should not think these disposed of all the evidences of Christmas; for the simple reason that we could not so much as remember all the evidences of Christmas. If a thousand more memories of it were thus explained, we should know there were a million more not explained. This is the first thing about Santa Claus. He is a tradition; that is, he is a fact. We may not know where he came from; but we know what he is. And if anybody says that he is heathen, I answer, with authority, that he is not.

The second thing misunderstood is the right kind of agnosticism; our ignorance about fairy tales refers back to that ultimate ignorance about life which makes life itself a fairy tale. Some complain that parents will not tell their children whether Santa Claus exists or not. The parents do not tell them for the excellent reason that the parents do not know. Those who have thought their way deepest into the mysteries of man's life in nature have generally tended to the idea that there were principles, and very probably personal principles, behind the energies in places, seasons, occupations, and periods of life. These speculations have generally, and perhaps wisely, been left indefinite and separated from the clear religious doctrines needed for the conduct of life. But they are quite sufficiently suggestive to make agnosticism cut, as I have said, both ways; and make a philosophical father at least as doubtful of rationalist explanations as of supernatural tales. He knows precious little more than the child knows. Parents sleep all night, and generally more heavily than children. And rationalistic parents sleep all day as well.

The third point is more obvious, but even more neglected; here it need only be mentioned to correct what has gone before. It should always be remembered that dogmatic and authoritative religions spend much of their time rather in restraining superstitions than in encouraging them; and that such enthusiasms as that which Protestants call 'Mariolatry' generally display all the merits and defects of widespread democratic movements. If saints such as St Nicholas of the Children do not exist, they were not a priestly deception, but an erroneous public opinion.

The fourth fact it is necessary to realise is that when the faithful in any real religion say that a certain thing historically happened once, they do not feel it as inconsistent with the idea that it actually happens constantly. If Tintoretto or Veronese painted himself, his family, his friends, his dog, in the same room with the Virgin and Child, it was because he really thought that these things could be in a room together: in other words, that though that Child had grown up and lived and been crucified by the princes of the world, He still really was a child, and His Mother the mother of a child. In the same way, if there is anything in the ingenious suggestion that Santa Claus bringing presents has a trace of the Wise Men bringing gifts to Bethlehem, there is no inconsistency in the Christian mind between his historically and literally having brought gifts on that occasion, and his really and truly bringing gifts every 25th of December. The heathen mind, now ruling our society, must accept it as a paradox.

The last point to remember is that, in these things, form is everything. You can 're-state' doctrine, though it is not being done very intelligently, because one clear logical meaning can be put in many verbal forms. You cannot 're-state' a vision. You can express the same thought in Greek, or in Turkish, or in Norman-French. But you cannot express the same thought in Greek architecture and Turkish architecture and Norman architecture. Hence all attempts to clothe Santa Claus in the symbols of other religions or older civilisations sin against the first principles of poetry. Santa Claus may have brought his presents from the East or his reindeers from the North; but he has brought them to our house. And the only test of whether he is genuine is whether he is recognised.

A FURTHER THOUGHT ⊰

The child who doubts about Santa Claus has insomnia. The child who believes has a good night's rest.

THE MODERN SCROOGE ⊰

Mr Vernon-Smith, of Trinity, and the Social Settlement, Tooting, author of 'A Higher London' and 'The Boyg System at Work', came to the conclusion, after looking through his select and even severe library, that Dickens's 'Christmas Carol' was a very suitable thing to be read to charwomen. Had they been men they would have been forcibly subjected to Browning's 'Christmas Eve' with exposition, but chivalry spared the charwomen, and Dickens was funny, and could do no harm. His fellow worker Wimpole would read things like 'Three Men in a Boat' to the poor; but Vernon-Smith regarded this as a sacrifice of principle, or (what was the same thing to him) of dignity. He would not encourage them in their vulgarity; they should have nothing from him that was not literature. Still Dickens was literature after all; not literature of a high order, of course, not thoughtful or purposeful literature, but literature quite fitted for charwomen on Christmas Eve.

He did not, however, let them absorb Dickens without due antidotes of warning and criticism. He explained that Dickens was not a writer of the first rank, since he lacked the high seriousness of Matthew Arnold. He also feared that they would find the characters of Dickens terribly exaggerated. But they did not, possibly because they were meeting them every day. For among the poor there are still exaggerated characters; they do not go to the Universities to be universified. He told the charwomen, with progressive brightness, that a mad wicked old miser like Scrooge would be really quite impossible now; but as each of the charwomen had an uncle or a grandfather or a father-in-law who was exactly like Scrooge, his cheerfulness was not shared. Indeed, the lecture as a whole lacked something of his firm and elastic touch, and towards the end he found himself rambling, and in a sort of abstraction, talking to them as if they were his fellows. He caught himself saying quite mystically that a spiritual plane (by which he meant his plane) always looked to those on the sensual or Dickens plane, not merely austere, but desolate. He said, quoting Bernard Shaw, that we could all go to heaven just as we can all go to a classical concert, but if we did it would bore us. Realizing that he was taking his flock far out of their depth, he ended somewhat hurriedly, and was soon receiving that generous applause which is a part of the profound ceremonialism of the working classes. As he made his way to the door three people stopped him, and he answered them heartily enough, but with an air of hurry which he would not have dreamed of showing to people of his own class. One was a little schoolmistress who told him with a sort of feverish meekness that she was troubled because an Ethical Lecturer had said that Dickens was not really Progressive; but she thought he was Progressive; and surely he *was* Progressive. Of what being Progressive was she had no more notion than a whale. The second person implored him for a subscription to some soup kitchen or cheap meal; and his refined features sharpened; for this, like literature, was a matter of principle with him. 'Quite the wrong method', he said, shaking his head and pushing past. 'Nothing any good but the Boyg system.' The third stranger, who was male, caught him on the step as he came out into the snow and starlight; and asked him point blank for money. It was a part of Vernon-Smith's principles that all such persons are prosperous impostors; and like a true mystic he held to his principles in defiance of his five senses, which told him that the night was freezing and the man very thin and weak. 'If you come to the Settlement between four and five on Friday week,' he said, 'inquiries will be made.' The man stepped back into the snow with a not ungraceful gesture as of apology; he had frosty silver hair, and his lean face, though in shadow, seemed to wear something like a smile. As Vernon-Smith stepped briskly into the street, the man stooped down as if to do up his bootlace. He was, however, guiltless of any such dandyism; and as the young philanthropist stood pulling on his gloves with some particularity, a heavy snowball was suddenly smashed into his face. He was blind for a black instant; then as some of the snow fell, saw faintly, as in a dim mirror of ice or dreamy crystal, the lean man bowing with the elegance of a dancing master, and saying amiably, 'A Christmas box.' When he had quite cleared his face of snow the man had vanished.

For three burning minutes Cyril Vernon-Smith was nearer to the people and more their brother than he had been in his whole high-stepping pedantic existence; for if he did not love a poor man, he hated one. And you never really regard a labourer as your equal until you can quarrel with him. 'Dirty cad!' he muttered. 'Filthy fool! Mucking with snow like a beastly baby! When will they be civilized? Why, the very state of the street is a disgrace and a temptation to such tomfools. Why isn't all this snow cleared away and the street made decent?'

To the eye of efficiency, there was, indeed, something to complain of in the condition of the road. Snow was banked up on both sides in white walls, and towards the other and darker end of the street even rose into a chaos of low colourless hills. By the time he reached them he was nearly knee deep, and was in a far from philanthropic frame of mind. The solitude of the little streets was as strange as their white obstruction, and before he had ploughed his way much further he was convinced that he had taken a wrong turning, and fallen upon some formless suburb unvisited before. There was no light in any of the low, dark houses; no light in anything but the blank emphatic snow. He was modern and morbid; hellish isolation hit and held him suddenly; anything human would have relieved the strain, if it had been only the leap of a garotter. Then the tender human touch came indeed; for another snowball struck him, and made a star on his back. He turned with fierce joy, and ran after a boy escaping; ran with dizzy and violent speed, he knew not for how long. He wanted the boy; he did not know whether he loved or hated him. He wanted humanity; he did not know whether he loved or hated it.

As he ran he realized that the landscape around him was changing in shape though not in colour. The houses seemed to dwindle and disappear in hills of snow as if buried; the snow seemed to rise in tattered outlines of crag and cliff and crest, but he thought nothing of all these impossibilities until the boy turned to bay. When he did he saw the child was queerly beautiful, with gold red hair, and a face as serious as complete happiness. And when he spoke to the boy his own question surprised him, for he said for the first time in his life, 'What am I doing here?' And the little boy, with very grave eyes, answered, 'I suppose you are dead.'

He had (also for the first time) a doubt of his spiritual destiny. He looked round on a towering landscape of frozen peaks and plains, and said, 'Is this hell?' And as the child stared, but did not answer, he knew it was heaven.

All over that colossal country, white as the world round the Pole, little boys were playing, rolling each other down dreadful slopes, crushing each other under falling cliffs; for heaven is a place where one can fight for ever without hurting. Smith suddenly remembered how happy he had been as a child, rolling about on the safe sandhills around Conway.

Right above Smith's head, higher than the cross of St Paul's, but curving over him like the hanging blossom of a harebell, was a cavernous crag of snow. A hundred feet below him, like a landscape seen from a balloon, lay snowy flats as white and as far away. He saw a little boy stagger, with many catastrophic slides, to that toppling peak; and seizing another little boy by the leg, send him flying away down to the distant silver plains. There he sank and vanished in the snow as if in the sea; but coming up again like a diver rushed madly up the steep once more, rolling before him a great gathering snowball, gigantic at last, which he hurled back at the mountain crest, and brought both the boy and the mountain down in one avalanche to the level of the vale. The other boy also sank like a stone, and also rose again like a bird, but Smith had no leisure to concern himself with this. For the collapse of that celestial crest had left him standing solitary in the sky on a peak like a church spire.

He could see the tiny figures of the boys in the valley below, and he knew by their attitudes that they were eagerly telling him to jump. Then for the first time he knew the nature of faith, as he had just known the fierce nature of charity. Or rather for the second time, for he remembered one moment when he had known faith before. It was when his father had taught him to swim, and he had believed he could float on water not only against reason, but (what is so much harder) against instinct. Then he had trusted water; now he must trust air.

He jumped. He went through air and then through snow with the same blinding swiftness. But as he buried himself in solid snow like a bullet he seemed to learn a million things and to learn them all too fast. He knew that the whole world is a snowball, and that all the stars are snowballs. He knew that no man will be fit for heaven till he loves solid whiteness as a little boy loves a ball of snow.

He sank and sank and sank . . . and then, as usually happens in such cases, woke up, with a start—in the street. True, he was taken up for a common drunk, but (if you properly appreciate his conversion) you will realize that he did not mind; since the crime of drunkenness is infinitely less than that of spiritual pride, of which he had really been guilty.

V

The Turkey and
the Turk

THE MUMMER'S PLAY

THE TURKEY AND THE TURK
The Mummer's Play

FATHER CHRISTMAS:

Here am I, Father Christmas; well you know it,
    Though critics say it fades, my Christmas Tree,
Yet was it Dickens who became my poet
    And who the Dickens may the critics be?

ST GEORGE:

I am St George, whose cross in scutcheon scored,
    Red as the Rose of England on me glows,
The Dragon who would pluck it, found this sword (*draws sword*)
    Which is the thorn upon the English Rose.

THE DOCTOR:

I am the Doctor from Berlin. I kill
    Germs and diseases upon handsome terms
—There are so many ways of being ill—
    Some trust the Germans. Some prefer the Germs.

THE TURKISH KNIGHT:

I am the Turkish Knight: to sink and rise
    In every Mummer's Play has been my work.
I am that Wrath that falls but never flies,
    A Turkish Knight—but a most knightly Turk.

THE PRINCESS OF THE MOUNTAINS:

I am the Princess come from mountains shady
    That are the world's last wall against the Turk.
I had to come; or there would be no lady
    In this remarkable dramatic work.

(*ENTER Father Christmas with Christmas
Pudding, Turkey, Flagons, etc.*)

I will not drink; let the great flagon here
Till the great toasts are drunk, stand where it is.
But Christmas pudding comes but once a year

But many times a day. And none amiss (*cuts off a piece*).
The Christmas Pudding, round as the round sky,
Speckled with better things than stars.

DOCTOR (*rushes in and arrests his hand*):
                                        Forgive
My haste. But men who eat that pudding die.

FATHER CHRISTMAS:
And men who do not eat it do not live (*eats*).

DOCTOR:
Our last proofs show, for perils that appal,
A Christmas pudding is a cannon ball.
But you grow old—

FATHER CHRISTMAS:
                        And you grow always new
And every year you take a different view.
My every Christmas brings, with change and chills,
New doctors' doctrines with new doctors' bills.
Next year this pudding where I plant my knife
Will be the only food sustaining life.
The proverb holds; who shall decide or choose
When doctors' disagree—with their own views?
Your drugs turn poisons and your poisons food.
And still this round and solid fact holds good—
While with themselves the doctors disagree
No Christmas pudding disagrees with me.

DOCTOR:
Progress is change; so is the whole world's youth
Afoot betimes to catch the newest truth,
While you in night-long wassail waste your breath
The early bird catches the worm of death,
Conquers the grave; and doth the secret know
Of life immortal.

FATHER CHRISTMAS:
                        For a month or so.
That, too, will change. Soon you will tell us all

That early rising is a daily fall,
That fever waits in fiery morning skies,
And Bed is the most bracing exercise.
You'll find for sluggards some more pleasing term
And cry 'The Early Bird catches the Germ'.

(*ENTER the Princess of the Mountains.*)

PRINCESS:

Save me and harbour me, all Christian folk,
For I am fleeing from the heathen might.
My mountain city is a trail of smoke,
My track is trampled by the Turkish Knight.
Already where I sink they shake the ground,
The flying towers, the horsemen of Mahound.

DOCTOR:

Mahound. More properly Muhammad. Quaint!
The wars of creeds—or demons—smoke and smother.
Each of the demons calls himself a saint
—Until two men can tolerate each other.

PRINCESS:

So were we taught by many Turkish kings
To tolerate intolerable things.

FATHER CHRISTMAS:

I have a creed. Its name is charity
And at my table all men may agree.

PRINCESS:

Folk of the West, bethink you, far from strife,
Through what more weary ages than you think,
Our broken swords covered your carving knife
And with our blood you bought the wine you drink,
That you might ply your kindlier Christmas work
And kill the Turkey while we killed the Turk.

FATHER CHRISTMAS:

I see one from the mountains ride amain
Who rather comes to slay than to be slain.

(ENTER Turkish Knight.)

TURKISH KNIGHT:

  I am the master of the sons of battle,
  The cohorts of the Crescent of the night,
  I for whom queens are slaves and slaves are cattle,
  I claim this queen and slave out of my right.
  I have burned her town and slain her sire in strife,
  Is there a better way to earn a wife?

PRINCESS:

  A wife! This Turkish dog, like sheep in pen,
  May herd a hundred wives—or bondwomen.

DOCTOR:

  Consider. Set above the smoke of passion
  Where high philosophy and reason reign,
  I can give counsel in a cooler fashion
  Who am the friend of peace, the foe of pain.
  Consider—should this gentleman insist—
  He might be worse than a polygamist.

PRINCESS:

  What could be worse, and what unworthier!

DOCTOR:

  He might, like Bluebeard, be a widower.
  The habit which enjoys a hundred wives
  Suggests at least, that every wife—survives.

PRINCESS:

  Such are not things that such as I survive,
  Nor shall such bridal see us both alive,
  Nor I consent—

TURKISH KNIGHT:

          Nor did I ask consent.
  I did not ask your banner to be rent,
  Your sire to fall, your battle-line to break,
  I do not ask for anything I take.

DOCTOR:

She will find comfort in Philosophy.

FATHER CHRISTMAS:

You were right, Doctor; I am old. Woe's me,
My knife is a clown's sword for cutting grease (*flings down
his carving-knife*).

DOCTOR (*looking piously upward*):

Peace! Is not this the certain road to Peace?

(*ENTER St George.*)

ST GEORGE:

Stop! For the doors are shut upon your treason,
I, George of Merry England, bar the way.
Not all so easily, not for a season,
You brave the anger of the saints at bay.
Red shall your cohorts be, your Crescent faint.
The hour you find—what will provoke a Saint.

DOCTOR:

Who is this mad Crusader?

FATHER CHRISTMAS (*lifting his flagon*):

He is come!
Let burst the trumpets, dance upon the drum!
Shout till you deafen the dead! I drain the flagon.
England in arms! St George that beat the Dragon!

DOCTOR:

You dream, old dotard, and your drunken tales
Are fumes of Yuletide vintages and ales.
The wine is in your head. Water and wine.
A Dragon! Snapdragon is more your line.

FATHER CHRISTMAS:

It may be. Who shall choose between us twain
Wine in the head or water on the brain?
But what of you, most prudent paragon,
You are as frightened of the snapdragon
As of the dragon, that St George has beaten,
More scared to eat than he was to be eaten.

ST GEORGE:

    At least I come in time to do redress
    On a new Dragon for a new Princess.

TURKISH KNIGHT:

    Sir, if my hundred wives indeed be sheep
    I am the shepherd, who can count and keep,
    And I keep this; had you a hundred lives
    This sword should teach you to respect my wives.

ST GEORGE:

    I will respect your widows.

TURKISH KNIGHT:

                  They that keep
    The oracles of the Prophet see you sleep
    Dead on your shield.

ST GEORGE:

              I bear upon my shield
    Death, and a certain lesson how to die—
    Your Prophet lived too late to prophesy.

    (Turkish Knight rushes forward.)

PRINCESS:

    See how the face of your strange Doctor sneers!

DOCTOR:

    How should Peace stay when Piety appears
    And men do murder for a change of words?
    Yet might the Peace be held. Ere you cross swords
    Knights of the Cross and Crescent, count the loss—

ST GEORGE:

    Two swords in crossing make the sign of the cross
    That frightens fiends.

    (Doctor leaps back from the clash of swords.)

              He's wounded in the hand;
    Doctor, a Doctor—let the battle stand.

DOCTOR:

I am a doctor, sir, and I can cure
Complaints and maladies such Turks endure,
In Turkish camps where air and water taints—

TURKISH KNIGHT:

You will find maladies, but not complaints.

DOCTOR:

But who will pay me if I cure the Turk?

ST GEORGE:

This hand will give you pay, which gives you work.

*(He hangs his Red Cross shield up behind
the Turkish Knight and Doctor.)*

ST GEORGE:

For proof that Christian men war not as cattle
Above my foeman's head I hang my shield,
That shows far off o'er hideous wastes of battle
My sword has shattered but my shield has healed.

FATHER CHRISTMAS:

They say to every shield there are two sides.
So shall our champion show them as he rides,
And milder servants follow him in fight,
The Red Cross nurses to the Red Cross Knight.

DOCTOR:

Nurses and knights and all your chivalry
Would still be barren mercies but for me.
While you with liberal words would mend the Turk,
The healing hand of Science does your work,
While you show generous gestures, vague or grand
The healing hand of Science finds a hand.

*(Produces a Mailed Fist—any sort of
big pantomime glove of armour.)*

FATHER CHRISTMAS:

Here is the sort of trick the doctors love
To take a hand and give us back a glove.

TURKISH KNIGHT:

What would you do? I do not understand.

DOCTOR:

The Gauntlet shall be mightier than the hand,
Science has found the hand of your desire
An iron hand, a hand for flinging fire,
A mailed fist, the ensign of your legions,
And from the fingers of it flames shall go,
Smoke and thick flames that poison vasty regions,
And blight the fields as well as blight the foe.
Fool and fantastic in your red-cross coat,
A more than human hand is at your throat,
A hand that chokes.

ST GEORGE:

           I know that this is sure
Whatever man can do, man can endure,
Though you shall loose all laws of fight, and fashion
A torture-chamber from a tilting-yard,
Though iron hard as doom grow hot as passion,
Man shall be hotter, man shall be more hard,
And when an army in your hell-fire faints,
You shall find martyrs who were never saints.

DOCTOR:

I am weary of your sainthood. If you knew
You would, as even I do, quake. But you
Who in a painted halo put reliance
Fear naught.

ST GEORGE:

       Not even the healing hand of science.

DOCTOR (*furiously*):

Then at him, wound him, waste him utterly (*they fight*).

TURKISH KNIGHT:

Ere I could wound him he has wounded me.

69

PRINCESS:

The Turk is wounded in the leg—

FATHER CHRISTMAS:

Well fought!

TURKISH KNIGHT:

A Doctor, quick, a Doctor! It is naught,
To heal such scathe should be a petty task.
I answer for my answering of it. Ask
The Princess of the Mountains, for she knows,
How long wars wage in Eastern sands or snows.
No splitting of a slender tilting lance
For a crowd's gaping or a lady's glance,
War to the knife!

DOCTOR:

The surgeon's knife, my lord
The surgeon's knife is mightier than the sword.
Answer me now, old driveller, as you can,
When your great carving-knife has cured a man,
Or if these bones the war-dogs crush and crunch
Can be patched up with pudding or with punch.
Lady, I tell you all your mountain dead
Who on Kossovo of the Blackbirds bled,
There where the hero dies as a dog dies,
Might have re-risen as this man shall rise,
Answer me now, proud lady, as you can
Does Science help? Can Science save a man?
What do you see, for all your savage pride?

PRINCESS:

I see it always helping the wrong side.

FATHER CHRISTMAS (*to St George*):

This is not just. You fight not one but three.
I think that you grow wearier than he.

PRINCESS:

Why should we patch this pirate up again?
Why should you always win, and win in vain?
Bid him not cut the leg, but cut the loss.

ST GEORGE:

I will not fire upon my own Red Cross.

PRINCESS:

If you lay there, would he let *you* escape?

ST GEORGE:

I am his Conqueror and not his ape.

DOCTOR:

Be not so sure of conquering. He shall rise
On lighter feet, on feet that vault the skies.
Science shall make a mighty foot and new,

(*Produces a sort of pantomine leg in armour and with wings*)

Light as the feather feet of Perseus flew,
Long as the seven-leagued boots in tales gone by,
This shall bestride the sea and ride the sky.
Thus shall he fly, and beat above your nation
The clashing pinions of Apocalypse,
Ye shall be deep-sea fish in pale prostration
Under the sky-foam of his flying ships.

(*The Turkish Knight advances with the
new leg, to fight again.*)

When terror above your cities, dropping doom,
Shall shut all England in a lampless tomb,
Your windows and your orphans now forlorn
Shall be no safer than the dead they mourn.
When all their lights grow dark, their lives grow grey,
What will those widows and those orphans say?

ST GEORGE:

St George for Merry England!

(*They fight again, with more doubtful effect, but St George at
last smites the Turkish Knight on the head and he falls.*)

PRINCESS:

Down is the Crescent and its crest abased!

DOCTOR:

A Head is very easily replaced.

FATHER CHRISTMAS:

More of this ironmongery that he hires.

DOCTOR:

Here is a Head no headache ever tires
Which never wants its hair cut, singed or curled,
The Business Head of all the Working World.

(*Produces pantomime head of a German with a spiked helmet
and spectacles—perhaps rather like the Doctor's own.*)

FATHER CHRISTMAS:

Shall we again grant respite to our foe?

ST GEORGE:

I tell you Yes, man!

(*The Turkish Knight suddenly lifts himself on his elbow.*)

TURKISH KNIGHT:

And I tell you No.
I'll have no more of your pale wizardry,
Leave me my wounded head and let me be.

DOCTOR:

What do you mean? A wound is only pain.
And why should I who twice, and now again,
Lead you to conquer, leave you now to die?

TURKISH KNIGHT:

Something may conquer. It will not be I.
If always thus you mend me when I fall,
There will be nothing of myself at all.
You arm me and you tame me and you trim.
Each time I gain a tool and lose a limb.
In wings and wheels all that I was will fade
And I shall be a monster You have made.

DOCTOR:

You hoped to have his head when you began.

TURKISH KNIGHT:

Base leech, I hoped to be the better man
And not the better mantrap. Leave alone!
I hoped to have his head—and keep my own (*rousing himself*)

72

When I came riding from the tents of morning
Clean as an arrow from my bended bow,
I had not need of such dead things' adorning,
No, by the panoply of the Prophet, no! (*rises*)
Lady, if we be less than you in love,
At least our hate as high as yours shall stand.
And I have lost. The Devil take my glove (*flings away the
mailed hand*).
And George of Merry England take my hand.

PRINCESS:

Now is the Turkish Knight a knight at least.

DOCTOR:

A Knight! They will be snivelling for a priest
To wed you to your Red Cross cut-throat here,
With all the mummeries of Faith—and Fear—
To suit this medieval mummery.
These fighting-cocks are caught in—Chivalry!
That in a tangle of fantastic rules
Makes them first foes, then friends, and always fools:
I would have rapt your souls to clearer rages,
On the top wave of Time, alive, alert,
I had done all that could outdare the ages.

FATHER CHRISTMAS (*poking him with the carving knife*):

Friend, did you ever laugh? And did it hurt?
No matter—if you cannot laugh, my friend,
You can be laughed at, let us laugh—and end.
Dragon and snapdragon alike take flight
With cockcrow. Take a slash at Turkish Knight.
Or take a slice of Turkey, as you choose,
And have the German Doctor for the goose—
And if the goose must cackle—if he tease
With talk of medieval mummeries,
Ask him what else but Mummery, I pray,
He asks from Mummers upon Christmas Day?

VI

The Spirit of Christmas

ESSAYS, A STORY AND COMMENT

THE CONTENTED MAN 🦅

True contentment is a thing as active as agriculture. It is the power of getting out of any situation all that there is in it. It is arduous and it is rare. The absence of this digestive talent is what makes so cold and incredible the tales of so many people who say they have been 'through' things; when it is evident that they have come out on the other side quite unchanged. A man might have gone 'through' a plum pudding as a bullet might go through a plum pudding; it depends on the size of the pudding—and the man. But the awful and sacred question is 'Has the pudding been through him?' Has he tasted, appreciated, and absorbed the solid pudding, with its three dimensions and its three thousand tastes and smells? Can he offer himself to the eyes of men as one who has cubically conquered and contained a pudding?

DICKENS AT CHRISTMAS 🦅

I have recently read in a modern novel a typical passage of the sort I referred to in relation to the red nose. In this case also some sensitive spirit could not endure existence because her surroundings were ugly. People often are; even sensitive spirits sometimes are; but they are so sensitive that nobody tells them so. In this novel there was a description of some indefensible old gentleman, some intolerable grandfather or unbearable great-uncle, gradually settling down into an armchair. Need I say that he slouched into it with the sluggish movement of mud? Need I say that he quaked like a quagmire? Need I say that he presented to the artistic temperament the image of some shapeless monster of the slime? This is quite correct; it may even be quite artistic; but it is not gay. It does not especially cheer us up, even at Christmas. In a word, it is not *funny*. Now let me turn to Dickens; and make a perfectly fair comparison. Sam Weller tells a story entirely devoted to the subject of a Fat Man. After explaining that the gentleman had not seen his own legs for years, he adds with impressive solemnity: 'If you 'ad put an exact model of 'is legs on the table in front of 'im, 'e wouldn't 'ave known 'em by sight'.

Now that is a poem. It uplifts the heart. It might naturally add to the joy of Christmas Day; or any day. It is actually much more of an exaggeration than the pessimist exaggeration which compares the old man to mud or a monster of the slime. But it is not only exaggerative; it is also creative. It is a new angle; we might say a new artistic vision. There is something aboriginally absurd in the idea of the old gentleman staring wild-eyed at his own legs; and half recalling something familiar about them; as if he were revisiting the landscape of his youth. There is something startlingly funny about the idea of a man's own legs being like a sort of public monument that he could never hope to see; and could only admire in an artistic reproduction. Now that is the essential quality that made Dickens great. He exaggerated, in the sense of making things greater than they were; but in the sense of making them more ridiculous than they were; more laughable than they were; more enjoyable than they were. He took common things and turned them into comic things; but the point is that the comedy was really a Christmas pantomime. It was an occasion for enjoyment and it was enjoyed. It makes the reader happier; just as if one of the lost and visionary legs had actually been thrust into his own Christmas stocking. Now I defy anybody to say that even the best of the modern satirical writers makes the reader happier. I deny that *Elmer Gantry* is a Christmas present. I deny that anybody wants Mr Dreiser thrust into his Christmas stocking. These works and these authors have all sorts of other valuable qualities, no doubt, but I am talking about Christmas; and why it is that people want to talk about Dickens at Christmas. The reason is in two sentences. The thing he did may or may not be suitable for all purposes; but it is suitable for Christmas. The thing he did may or may not be superior in all respects; but it has never been done since.

CHRISTMAS MUST GO ✎

Christmas is utterly unsuited to the modern world. It presupposes the possibility of families being united, or reunited, and even of the men and women who chose each other being on speaking terms. Thus thousands of young adventurous spirits, ready to face the facts of human life, and encounter the vast variety of men and women as they really are, ready to fly to the ends of the earth and tolerate every alien or accidental quality in cannibals or devil-worshippers, are cruelly forced to face an hour, nay sometimes even two hours, in the society of Uncle George; or some aunt from Cheltenham whom they do not particularly like. Such abominable tortures cannot be tolerated in a time like ours. That larger brotherhood, that truer sensibility, has already taught every spirited young lady (of sufficient wealth and leisure) to be thrilled at the prospect of having breakfast with a gun-man, lunch with a Sheik, and dinner with an Apache in Paris. It is intolerable that such sensibility should suffer the shock of the unexpected appearance of her own mother, or possibly her own child. It was never supposed that Parents were included in the great democratic abstraction called People. It was never supposed that brotherhood could extend to brothers.

Anyhow, Christmas is unsuited to modern life; its concentration in the household was conceived without allowing for the size and convenience of the modern hotel; its inheritance of ceremonial ignored the present convention of unconventionality; its appeal to childhood was in conflict with the more liberal conception; that Bright Young Things should always feel as if they were old and talk as if they were dull. That freer and franker school of manners, which consists of being bored with everybody who is present and forgetting everybody who is absent, is insulted in its first part by the old custom of drinking healths or exchanging good wishes, and in its second part by the custom of writing letters or sending Christmas cards. Under the load of such old tribal or communal exchanges, it is impossible to preserve the fine shade, the delicate distinction that marks modern manners; the distinction by which the next-door neighbour in the street is forgotten, while the next-door neighbour at the dinner-table is only ignored. How could we expect to extend a tradition that depended upon hospitality, across that happy interlude in the modern fashionable world, which replaced hospitality by housebreaking? Some variation of phrase was doubtless essential; and, to speak strictly and pedantically, it was called gate-crashing when done by the upper classes and housebreaking when done by the lower classes. But the burglar drinking whisky of which he had not been invited to partake, and the Bright Young Thing drinking champagne of which she had not been invited to partake, unconsciously joined hands in one great forward and progressive urge, to sweep away the old superstition of hospitality. Hospitality has a hundred horrid implications anyhow; it implies that my home belongs to me more than it belongs to an interviewer from a syndicated millionaire newspaper in Detroit; and however heartily and affectionately I may entertain and embrace such an interviewer, there is still a queer atmospheric prejudice hovering in his mind, not to mention mine; the old uncanny and creepy superstition that he is in somebody else's house. He would undoubtedly be freed from this embarrassment if we met in a large hotel, or a larger and even more impersonal tea-shop, or in a public library, or in a post office, or in the draughty corridors of a tube station. The very names of these places will suggest that richer warmth, that fuller fraternity, that tingling humanity in all human contacts, which comes to men the moment they have abandoned private property. Anyhow, it is unnecessary to extend the list of evidences that Christmas does not fit in with this fuller and more liberated life. Christmas must go. Christmas is utterly unsuited to the great future that is now opening before us. Christmas is not founded on the great communal conception which can only find its final expression in Communism. Christmas does not really help the higher and healthier and more vigorous expansion of Capitalism. Christmas cannot be expected to fit in with modern hopes of a great social future. Christmas is a contradiction of modern thought. Christmas is an obstacle to modern progress. Rooted in the past, and even the remote past, it cannot assist a world in which the ignorance of history is the only clear evidence of the knowledge of science. Born among miracles reported from two thousand years ago, it cannot expect to impress that sturdy common sense which can withstand the plainest and most palpable evidence for miracles happening at this moment. Dealing with matters purely psychic, it naturally has no interest for psychologists; having been the moral atmosphere of millions for more than sixteen centuries, it is of no interest to an age concerned with averages and statistics. It is concerned with the happiest of births and is the chief enemy of Eugenics; it carries along with it a tradition of voluntary virginity, yet it contains no really practical hints for compulsory sterilisation. At every point it is found to be in opposition to that great onward movement, by which we know that ethics will evolve into something that is more ethical and free from all ethical distinctions. Christmas is not modern; Christmas is not Marxian; Christmas is not made on the pattern of that great age of the Machine, which promises to the masses an epoch of even greater happiness and prosperity than that to which it has brought the masses at this moment. Christmas is medieval; having arisen in the earlier days of the Roman Empire. Christmas is a superstition. Christmas is a survival of the past.

But why go on piling up the praises of Christmas? All its gifts and glories are externally symbolised in that fact already sufficiently summarised; that it is a nuisance to all the people talking the particular nonsense of our own time. It is an irritation to all men who have lost their instincts; which is very truly the intellectual equivalent of losing their senses. It is a perpetual annoyance to the cads who are not only captains of industry, but captains of information and international news, and everything else in the present paradise of cads. It is a challenge to caddishness, because it reminds us of a more gracious world of courtesy; and of customs which assumed a sort of dignity in human relations. It is a puzzle to pedants whose cold hatred involves them in a continual contradiction; who are distracted between denouncing Christmas because it is a Mass, or purely Popish mummery, and trying to prove at the same time that it is entirely heathen, and was once as admirable as everything else invented by the pirates of heathen Scandinavia. It stands up unbroken and baffling; for us one thing, for them a confusion of inconsistencies; and it judges the modern world. Christmas must go. It is going. In fact it is going strong.

CHRISTMAS AND GEOFFREY CHAUCER

A Christmas dinner, as described by a modern minor poet, would almost certainly be a study in acute agony: the unendurable dullness of Uncle George; the cacophonous voice of Aunt Adelaide. But Chaucer, who sat down at the table with the Miller and the Pardoner, could have sat down to a Christmas dinner with the heaviest uncle or the shrillest aunt. He might have been amused at them, but he would never have been angered by them, and certainly he would never have insulted them in irritable little poems. And the reason was partly spiritual and partly practical; spiritual because he had, whatever his faults, a scheme of spiritual values in their right order, and knew that Christmas was more important than Uncle George's anecdotes; and practical because he had seen the great world of human beings, and knew that wherever a man wanders among men, in Flanders or France or Italy, he will find that the world largely consists of Uncle Georges. This imaginative patience is the thing that men want most in the modern Christmas, and if they wish to learn it I recommend them to read Chaucer.

It is the greatest glory of the Christian tradition that it has incorporated so many Pagan traditions. But it is most glorious of all, to my mind, when they are popular traditions. And the best and most obvious example is the way in which Christianity did incorporate, in so far as it did incorporate, the old human and heathen conception of the Winter Feast. There are, indeed, two profound and mysterious truths to be balanced here. The first is that what was then heathen was still human; that is, it was both mystical and material; it expressed itself in sacred substances and sacramental acts; it understood the mystery of trees and waters and the holy flame. And the other, which will be a much more tactless and irritating assertion, is that while a thing is heathen it is not yet completely human. But the point here is that the Pagan element in Christmas came quite natural to Christians, because it was not in fact very far from Christianity.

Take, for example, the whole fundamental idea of a Winter Feast. There is a perfectly natural parallel between a religion that defies the world and a ritual that defies the weather. Heathenism in the sense of hedonism, the concentration of the mind on pure pleasure as such, would chiefly concentrate on the conception of a Summer Feast. But in winter even a rich man receives some faint hint of the problem of a poor man; he may avoid being hungry, but he cannot always avoid being cold. To choose that moment of common freezing for the assertion of common fraternity is, in its own intrinsic nature, a foreshadowing of what we call the Christian idea. It involves the suggestion that joy comes from within and not from without. It involves the suggestion that peril and the potentiality of pain are themselves a ground of gratitude and rejoicing. It involves the suggestion that even when we are merely Pagans we are not merely Pantheists. We are not merely Nature-worshippers; because Man smiles when Nature frowns. It has always involved, under varying limitations in varying societies, the idea of hospitality; especially hospitality to the stranger and generally to the poor. Of course, there are perfectly natural reasons for wanting to drink wine or warm ourselves at the fire in winter; but that is not an answer, except to those who already have the ill-informed prejudice that Christianity must be opposed to things merely because they are natural. The point is in making a point of it; the special interest is in the special occasion;

in the fact that during the Winter Feast, whether Pagan or Christian, there always was, in some degree, the idea of extending the enjoyment to others; of passing round the wine or seating the wanderer by the hearth. It is no controversial point against the Christians that they felt they could take up and continue such traditions among the Pagans; it only shows that the Christians knew a Christian thing when they saw it.

This real history of Christmas is very relevant to the real crisis of Christendom. We live in a terrible time of war and rumour of war; with a barbaric danger of the real reaction, that goes back not to the old form but to the old formlessness. International idealism in its effort to hold the world together, in a peace that can resist wars and revolutions, is admittedly weakened and often disappointed. I should say simply that it does not go deep enough. Christianity could draw life out of the depths of Paganism; but mere Modernism cannot draw on the depths of either. Charity is too much of a manufactured article; and too little of a natural product. The League of Nations is too new to be natural. The modern materialistic humanitarianism is too young to be vigorous. If we really wish to make vivid the horrors of destruction and mere disciplined murder, we must see them more simply as attacks on the hearth and the human family; and feel about Hitler as men felt about Herod. If we want to talk about poverty, we must talk about it as the hunger of a human being, a pain as positive as toothache; and not as the fall in wages or the failure of imports, or even the lowering of the economic standard of living. We must say first of the beggar, not that there is insufficient housing accommodation, but that he has nowhere to lay his head. We must say first of the human family, not that there are no jobs for them in the factory, but that there is no room for them in the inn. That is, we must talk of the human family in language as plain and practical and positive as that in which mystics used to talk of the Holy Family. We must learn again to use the naked words that describe a natural thing; and dispense for a moment with all those sociological polysyllables, with which an artificial society has learned to talk of it as an artificial thing. Then we shall draw on the driving force of many thousand years; and call up a real humanitarianism out of the depths of humanity.

As the Three Wise Men brought gifts to Bethlehem, so did the Three Wiser Men of that wiser world of which the new prophets tell us bring gifts to that city which is brighter than Bethlehem, which is or will be a perfect blend of Boston and Babylon and Birmingham, but perfecting the perfections of all three. The First King, who had once been known as the Radium King, had later risen to the title of the Aetherite King, being named after that great new metal so much more precious than gold and so much more sharp and piercing than steel. In that empire of knowledge and power, a precious metal was not merely dug up as a dog digs up a bone; but by scientific analysis and combination precipitated out of the void like frozen lightning; as if born within the mind of man. Nor was it childishly hoarded like gold in a casket, but wrought into a hundred shining shapes to delight and serve the child of all the ages; wheels of blinding speed or engines whose stature reached the stars; all the towering things that can be made by man were brought as toys before the child. And the Second King was the lord not of incense only, but of all the graduated odours of the great new science of scent; whereby men could manufacture the atmosphere about them and almost create a climate like men creating a sky. Clouds like the clouds of the morning and evening hung above their march like banners and all the scents of Asia passed through them like changing tunes. But these also were far removed from their rudimentary natural elements and being rarified by analysis had also something of the abstraction of music. And although the Third King in some sense continued with a faint tradition of burial and the bitterness of myrrh, the same adaptation had brought these things far beyond such rude and remote beginnings; for there went with him the chemical fires of crematoria and a lulling breath of lethal chambers; and his disinfectants were the most delightful in the world.

As the moving marble causeway across the desert bore the motionless groups nearer to their destination, they talked a little of the wide range of their gifts, and how they had been planned to express all the achievements of humanity; and hoped that nothing was lacking to that completeness.

'There is no reason why anything whatever should be lacking,' said the First King a little sharply, 'Now that our processes are perfected, there is nothing that cannot be done. We have only to perceive a lack and supply it.'

'The only danger is,' replied the Second King, 'that in such fulness we should not perceive anything lacking. Even in your vast and marvellous machinery some tiny screw may be loose.'

'It is strange that you should say so,' said the Last King, in his more funereal voice. 'I cannot get rid of a foolish sense that I may have lost some little thing or left it behind.'

And when they had come to the New Bethlehem, curiously enough, they noticed that the official in charge of the operations, an eminent electrical engineer whose name was Joseph, was walking rapidly to and fro with something of a worried or at least a puzzled look. He also had something of the air of trying to remember what he had forgotten. Presently the advance halted; and in front of them there seemed to be some fumbling of delay.

'I thought there was a hitch somewhere,' said the Second King, frowning. 'Now that we have learnt to leave nothing to nature, it is exasperating to be checked by some complication in our own arrangements. I shall make searching inquiries at once.'

He stepped forward and conferred briefly with the frowning Joseph; then he turned to them again, his own face wearing a frown. He scowled a moment at all that forest of gigantic gifts and then said curtly:

'I knew there was some mistake. They have neglected to procure a child.'

SNOW IN BETHLEHEM ❧

This is written amid fields of snow within a few days of Christmas. And when last I saw snow it was within a few miles of Bethlehem. The coincidence will serve as a symbol of something I have noticed all my life, though it is not very easy to sum up. It is generally the romantic thing that turns out to be the real thing, under the extreme test of realism. It is the sceptical and even rational legend that turns out to be entirely legendary. Everything I had been taught or told led me to regard snow in Bethlehem as a paradox, like snow in Egypt. Every rumour of realism, every indirect form of rationalism, every scientific opinion taken on authority and at third hand, had led me to regard the country where Christ was born solely as a sort of semi-tropical place with nothing but palm-trees and parasols. It was only when I actually looked at it that it looked exactly like a Christmas card.

THE HEART OF BETHLEHEM ⊰

The heart of Bethlehem is a cavern; the sunken shrine which is the traditional scene of the Nativity. Nine times out of ten these traditions are true, and this is wholly ratified by the truth about the countryside; for it is into such subterranean stables that the people have driven their cattle, and they are by far the likeliest places of refuge for such a homeless group. It is curious to consider what numberless and varied versions of the Bethlehem story have been turned into pictures. No man who understands Christianity will complain that they are all different from each other and all different from the truth, or rather the fact. It is the whole point of the story that it happened in one particular human place that might have been any particular human place; a sunny colonnade in Italy or a snow-laden cottage in Sussex. It is yet more curious that some modern artists have prided themselves on merely topographical truth; and yet have not made much of this truth about the dark and sacred place underground. It seems strange that they have hardly emphasized the one case in which realism really touches reality. There is something beyond expression moving to the imagination in the idea of the holy fugitives being brought lower than the very land; as if the earth had swallowed them; the glory of God like gold buried in the ground. Perhaps the image is too deep for art, even in the sense of dealing in another dimension. For it might be difficult for any art to convey simultaneously the divine secret of the cavern and the cavalcade of the mysterious kings, trampling the rocky plain and shaking the cavern roof. Yet the medieval pictures would often represent parallel scenes on the same canvas; and the medieval popular theatre, which the guildsmen wheeled about the streets, was sometimes a structure of three floors, with one scene above another. A parallel can be found in those tremendous lines of Francis Thompson:

> East, ah, east of Himalay
> Dwell the nations underground,
> Hiding from the shock of Day;
> From the sun's uprising sound.

But no poetry even of the greatest poets will ever express all that is hidden in that image of the light of the world like a subterranean sun; only these prosaic notes remain to suggest what one individual felt about Bethlehem.

I have rather rashly undertaken to write of the Spirit of Christmas; and it presents a preliminary difficulty about which I must be candid. People are very curious nowadays in their way of talking about 'the spirit' of a thing. There is, for example, a particular sort of prig who is always lecturing us about having the spirit of true Christianity, apart from all names and forms. As far as I can make out, he means the very opposite of what he says. He means that we are to go on using the names 'Christian' and 'Christianity', and so on, for something in which it is quite specially the spirit that is not Christian; something that is a sort of combination of the baseless optimism of an American atheist with the pacifism of a mild Hindoo. In the same way, we read a great deal about the Spirit of Christmas in modern journalism or commercialism; but it is really a reversal of the same kind. So far from preserving the essentials without the externals, it is rather preserving the externals where there cannot be the essentials. It means taking two mere material substances, like holly and mistletoe, and spreading them all over huge and homeless cosmopolitan hotels or round the Doric columns of impersonal clubs full of jaded and cynical old gentlemen; or in any other place where the actual spirit of Christmas is least likely to be. But there is also another way in which modern commercial complexity eats out the heart of the thing, while actually leaving the painted shell of it. And that is the much too elaborate system of dependence on buying and selling, and therefore on bustle and hustle; and the actual neglect of the new things that might be done by the old Christmas.

Normally, if anything were normal nowadays, it would seem a truism to say that Christmas has been a family festival. But it is now possible (as I have had the good or bad luck to discover) to earn a reputation for paradox simply by going on saying that truisms are true. In this case, of course, the reason, the only reasonable reason, was religious. It was concerned with a happy family because it was consecrated to the Holy Family. But it is perfectly true that many men saw the fact without specially feeling the reason. When we say the root was religious, we do not mean that Sam Weller was concentrated on theological values when he told the Fat Boy to 'put a bit on Christmas', into some object, probably edible. We do not mean that the Fat Boy had gone into a trance of mystical contemplation like a monk seeing a vision. We do not even mean that Bob Cratchit defended punch by saying he was only looking on the wine when it was yellow; or that Tiny Tim quoted Timothy. We only mean that they, including their author, would have confessed humbly and heartily that there was someone historically quite anterior to Mr Scrooge, who might be called the Founder of the Feast. But in any case, whatever the reason, all would have agreed about the result. Mr Wardle's feast centred in Mr Wardle's family; and none the less because the romantic shadows of Mr Winkle and Mr Snodgrass threatened to break it up for the formation of other families.

The Christmas season is domestic; and for that reason most people now prepare for it by struggling in tramcars, standing in queues, rushing away in trains, crowding despairingly into tea-shops, and wondering when or whether they will ever get home. I do not know whether some of them disappear for ever in the toy department or simply lie down and die in the tea-rooms; but by the look of them, it is quite likely. Just before the great festival of the home the whole population seems to have become homeless. It is the supreme triumph of industrial civilisation that, in the huge cities which seem to have far too many houses, there is a hopeless shortage of housing. For a long time past great numbers of our poor have become practically nomadic. We even confess the fact; for we talk of some of them as Street Arabs. But this domestic institution, in its present ironical phase, has gone beyond such normal abnormality. The feast of the family turns the rich as well as the poor into vagabonds. They are so scattered over the bewildering labyrinth of our traffic and our trade, that they sometimes cannot even reach the tea-shop; it would be indelicate, of course, to mention the tavern. They have a difficulty in crowding into their hotels, let alone separating to reach their houses. I mean quite the reverse of irreverence when I say that their only point of resemblance to the archetypal Christmas family is that there is no room for them at the inn.

Now Christmas is built upon a beautiful and intentional paradox; that the birth of the homeless should be celebrated in every home. But the other sort of paradox is not intentional and is certainly not beautiful. It is bad enough that we cannot altogether disentangle the tragedy of poverty. It is bad enough that the birth of the homeless, celebrated at hearth and altar, should sometimes synchronise with the death of the homeless in workhouses and slums. But we need not rejoice in this universal restlessness brought upon rich and poor alike; and it seems to me that in this matter we need a reform of the modern Christmas.

I will now emit another brilliant flash of paradox by remarking that Christmas occurs in the winter. That is, it is not only a feast dedicated to domesticity, but it is one deliberately placed under the conditions in which it is most uncomfortable to rush about and most natural to stop at home. But under the complicated conditions of modern conventions and conveniences, there arises this more practical and much more unpleasant sort of paradox. People have to rush about for a few weeks, if it is only to stay at home for a few hours. Now the old and healthy idea of such winter festivals was this; that people being shut in and besieged by the weather were driven back on their own resources; or, in other words, had a chance of showing whether there was anything in them. It is not certain that the reputation of our most fashionable modern pleasure-seekers would survive the test. Some dreadful exposures would be made of some such brilliant society favourites, if they were cut off from the power of machinery and money. They are quite used to having everything done for them; and even when they go to the very latest American dances, it seems to be mostly the negro musicians who dance. But anyhow, on the average of healthy humanity I believe the cutting off of all these mechanical connections would have a thoroughly enlivening and awakening effect. At present they are always accused of merely amusing themselves; but they are doing nothing so noble or worthy of their human dignity. Most of them by this time cannot amuse themselves; they are too used to being amused.

Christmas might be creative. We are told, even by those who praise it most, that it is chiefly valuable for keeping up ancient customs or old-fashioned games. It is indeed valuable for both those admirable purposes. But in the sense of which I am now speaking it might once more be possible to turn the truth the other way round. It is not so much old things as new things that a real Christmas might create. It might, for instance, create new games, if people were really driven to invent their own games. Most of the very old games began with the use of ordinary tools or furniture. So the very terms of tennis were founded on the framework of the old inn courtyard. So, it is said, the stumps in cricket were originally only the three legs of the milking-stool. Now we might invent new things of this kind, if we remembered who is the mother of invention. How pleasing it would be to start a game in which we scored so much for hitting the umbrella-stand or the dinner-wagon, or even the host and hostess; of course, with a missile of some soft material. Children who are lucky enough to be left alone in the nursery invent not only whole games, but whole dramas and life-stories of their own; they invent secret languages; they create imaginary families; they laboriously conduct family magazines. That is the sort of creative spirit that we want in the modern world; want both in the sense of desiring and in the sense of lacking it. If Christmas could become more domestic, instead of less, I believe there would be a vast increase in the real Christmas spirit; the spirit of the Child. But in indulging this dream we must once more invert the current convention into the form of a paradox. It is true in a sense that Christmas is the time at which the doors should be open. But I would have the doors shut at Christmas, or at least just before Christmas; and then the world shall see what we can do.

I cannot but remember, with something of a smile, that on an earlier and more controversial page of this book I have mentioned a lady who shuddered at the thought of the things perpetrated by my co-religionists behind closed doors. But my memory of it is mellowed by distance and the present subject, and I feel quite the reverse of controversial. I hope that lady, and all of her way of thinking, may also have the wisdom to close their doors; and discover that only when all the doors are closed the best thing will be found inside. If they are Puritans, whose religion is only based on the Bible, let it for once indeed be a Family Bible. If they are Pagans, who can accept nothing but the winter feast, let it at least be a family feast. The discordance or discomfort complained of by modern critics, in the family reunion, is not due to that mystical focal fire having been left burning, but to its having been left to go cold. It is because cold fragments of a once living thing are clumsily lumped together; it is no argument against making the thing alive. Christmas toys are incongruously dangled before heavy and heathen uncles who wish they were playing golf. But that does not alter the fact that they might become much brighter and more intelligent if they knew how to play with toys; and they are horrible bores about golf. Their dullness is only the last deadly product of the mechanical progress of organised and professional sports, in that rigid world of routine outside the home. When they were children, behind closed doors in the home, it is probable that nearly every one of them had day-dreams and unwritten dramas that belonged to them as much as Hamlet belonged to Shakespeare or Pickwick to Dickens. How much more thrilling it would be if Uncle Henry, instead of describing in detail all the strokes with which he ought to have got out of the bunker, were to say frankly that he had been on a voyage to the end of the world and had just caught the Great Sea-Serpent. How much more truly intellectual would be the conversation of Uncle William if, instead of telling us the point to which he had reduced his handicap, he could still say with conviction that he was King of the Kangaroo Islands, or Chief of the Rango Dango Redskins. These things, projected from within, were in almost all human spirits; and it is not normal that the inspiration of them should be so utterly crushed by the things without. Let it not be supposed for a moment that I also am among the tyrants of the earth, who would impose my own tastes, or force all the other children to play my own games. I have no disrespect for the game of golf; it is an admirable game. I have played it; or rather, I have played at it, which is generally regarded as the very opposite. By all means let the golfers golf and even the organisers organise, if their only conception of an organ is something like a barrel-organ. Let them play golf day after day; let them play golf for three hundred and sixty-four days, and nights as well, with balls dipped in luminous paint, to be pursued in the dark. But let there be one night when things grow luminous from within: and one day when men seek for all that is buried in themselves; and discover, where she is indeed hidden, behind locked gates and shuttered windows, and doors thrice barred and bolted, the spirit of liberty.

THE THREE GIFTS 〜

There were three things prefigured and promised by the gifts in the cave of Bethlehem concerning the Child who received them; that He should be crowned like a King: that He should be worshipped like a God; and that He should die like a man. And these things would sound like Eastern flattery, were it not for the third.

VII

Gloria in Profundis

A LAST POEM

GLORIA IN PROFUNDIS 🙚

There has fallen on earth for a token
A god too great for the sky.
He has burst out of all things and broken
The bounds of eternity:
Into time and the terminal land
He has strayed like a thief or a lover,
For the wine of the world brims over,
Its splendour is spilt on the sand.

Who is proud when the heavens are humble,
Who mounts if the mountains fall,
If the fixed stars topple and tumble
And a deluge of love drowns all—
Who rears up his head for a crown,
Who holds up his will for a warrant,
Who strives with the starry torrent,
When all that is good goes down?

For in dread of such falling and failing
The fallen angels fell
Inverted in insolence, scaling
The hanging mountain of hell:
But unmeasured of plummet and rod
Too deep for their sight to scan,
Outrushing the fall of man
Is the height of the fall of God.

Glory to God in the Lowest
The spout of the stars in spate—
Where the thunderbolt thinks to be slowest
And the lightning fears to be late:
As men dive for a sunken gem
Pursuing, we hunt and hound it,
The fallen star that has found it
In the cavern of Bethlehem.

SOURCES AND NOTES

The title of each piece follows the number of the page on which it appears, and this in turn is followed by details of its first publication. Subsequent appearances in collections and anthologies are not listed; where they occur, they can be found in John Sullivan's three volumes of Chesterton bibliography.

12 'Xmas Day' from GKC's notebook *circa* 1895, quoted in Masie Ward's *Gilbert Keith Chesterton* (Sheed and Ward, 1944). ☐ 12 'The Nativity' from *The Parents' Review*, 1897; revised in *The Commonwealth*, Jan. 1902. ☐ 13, 14 'A Christmas Carol' and 'Joseph' from *The Wild Knight* (Grant Richards, 1900). ☐ 15 'The Wise Men' from *The Daily News*, 25th Dec. 1905. ☐ 'Christmas That Is Coming' from *The Illustrated London News*, 29th Dec. 1906. ☐ 18 'The Christmas Ballads' from *The Daily News*, 25th Dec. 1901. ☐ 21 'Christmas Pudding' from *The Illustrated London News*, 29th Dec. 1906. ☐ 22 'Dickens' Christmas Tales' from the Introduction to *Christmas Books* by Charles Dickens (Everyman, 1907). ☐ 25 'Turkey' from *The Illustrated London News*, 29th Dec. 1906. ☐ 26 'Mock Turkey' from *The New Witness*, 24th Dec. 1920. ☐ 27 'Sausages and Stars' from *The Daily News*, 6th June 1903. ☐ 27 'The Shop of Ghosts' from *The Daily News*, 22nd Dec. 1906. ☐ 34, 35 'A Child of the Snows' and 'A Word' from *Poems* (Burns and Oates, 1915). ☐ 34, 37 'The House of Christmas' and 'The Truce of Christmas'' from *A Chesterton Calendar* (Kegan Paul, 1911). ☐ 38 'A Song of Gifts to God' from *The Pall Mall Magazine*, Dec. 1913. ☐ 42 'More Thoughts on Christmas' from *The Illustrated London News*, 27th Dec. 1913. ☐ 44 'Dickens Again' from *The Illustrated London News*, 21st Dec. 1912. ☐ 47 'A Christmas Present' from *The Daily News*, 28th Dec. 1907. ☐ 48 'The Theology of Christmas Presents' from *The Contemporary Review*, Jan. 1910. ☐ 52 'Christmas and the Professors' from *The Illustrated London News*, 18th Dec. 1909. ☐ 53 'Some Fallacies and Santa Claus' from *The Nation*, 7th Dec. 1912. ☐ 56 'A Further Thought' from *Magic* (Secker, 1913). ☐ 56 'The Modern Scrooge' from *The Daily News*, 25th Dec. 1909. ☐ 62 'The Turkey and the Turk' from *G.K.'s Weekly*, 5th Dec. 1925. ☐ 76 'The Contented Man' from *The Daily News*, 10th June, 1911. ☐ 76 'Dickens at Christmas' from a BBC Radio broadcast, 25th Dec. 1931. ☐ 77 'Christmas Must Go' from *G.K.'s Weekly*, 7th Dec. 1933. ☐ 80 'Christmas and Geoffrey Chaucer' from *The Illustrated London News*, 26th Dec. 1931. ☐ 81 'The Winter Feast' from *G.K.'s Weekly*, 2nd Jan. 1936. ☐ 83 'The New Christmas' from *G.K.'s Weekly*, 25th Dec. 1926. ☐ 84 'Snow in Bethlehem' from *The Illustrated London News*, 1920. ☐ 85 'The Heart of Bethlehem' from *The New Witness*, 8th Dec. 1922. ☐ 86 'The Spirit of Christmas' from *The Thing* (Sheed and Ward, 1929). 90 'The Three Gifts' from *G.K.'s Weekly*, 12th Dec. 1931. ☐ 93 'Gloria in Profundis', Number Five of *The Ariel Poems* (Faber and Gwyer, 1927).

INDEX OF TITLES

The titles of poems are printed in italics